undersea
work
systems

Ocean Engineering

Series Editor

Neil T. Monney
United States Naval Academy
Annapolis, Maryland

1. Undersea Work Systems, *by Howard R. Talkington*

Other volumes in preparation

undersea work systems

HOWARD R. TALKINGTON
U.S. Naval Ocean Systems Center
San Diego, California

MARCEL DEKKER, INC.   NEW YORK AND BASEL

Library of Congress Cataloging in Publication Data

Talkington, Howard R.
  Undersea work systems.

  (Ocean engineering; 1)
  Bibliography: p.
  Includes index.
  1. Ocean engineering.   I. Title.   II.   Series.
TC1645.T34   627'.7   80-25978
ISBN 0-8247-1226-9

MARCEL DEKKER, INC.
270 Madison Avenue, New York, New York 10016

Current printing (last digit):
10 9 8 7 6 5 4 3 2 1

PRINTED IN THE UNITED STATES OF AMERICA

To my family

Foreword

The key to opening the last frontier on earth rests in the hands of the ocean engineer. Ocean scientists provide the fundamental knowledge of the physical, chemical, and biological characteristics of the ocean environment. It is the task of the ocean engineer to build on this knowledge and provide the hardware systems that can unlock the enormous wealth of ocean resources. These resources—food, minerals, water, energy, routes for world commerce, and even space for seaward expansion of crowded coastal zones—are becoming critically important as our resources on land are pressed to their limits. The ocean engineer must provide a safe, cost-effective means of utilizing ocean resources, while at the same time protecting the environment to ensure a sustained yield of renewable resources. It is the intent of this series to tap the knowledge and experience of many of the foremost ocean engineers throughout the world, and bring to the reader the most current information available in this field. The series will encompass a broad range of engineering disciplines that with their application in the ocean environment comprise the field of "ocean engineering."

Neil T. Monney

Preface

As we turn increasingly to the sea to support our everyday needs, new concepts of equipment for exploration and exploitation must be evolved. For centuries, the oceans have been a highway for transportation and a storehouse for food. Now, as the demand for food increases, new improvements in harvesting methods must be developed. The potential of energy from offshore oil and gas, and the rich rewards from extraction of minerals from deep sea nodules, make developments in performing work within the sea an increasingly important necessity. New work systems, employing new concepts and applying new materials, are providing the foundation for a new ocean industry. These undersea work systems are the subject matter of this book.

The material in this book is intended to provide the reader with an understanding of undersea work systems, how they are conceived, designed, fabricated, and operated. First, we must acknowledge that undersea work systems are developed to perform useful work within the sea. To meet this objective, the overriding requirement is that the tasks to be conducted for undersea operations must be thoroughly understood. Work systems can then be designed taking into account the operators, the surface and subsurface environments, the support craft, as well as the work functions to be performed within the sea.

viii

The potential designer or operator is led through the various phases of development and operation of undersea work systems: task definition; concept formulation based upon functional requirements; selection of components and materials; and assembly and testing in preparation for operations. A description of systems currently available is also provided, along with some examples of their operations while performing particularly complicated tasks. Finally, a proposed undersea work system is synthesized, using the methodology previously developed, to meet the task requirements of a complex, real-world undersea project.

A bibliography is included at the end of each chapter for those who may wish to delve further into particular subjects.

Numerous companies and individuals have assisted in the preparation of this book, by providing data on their products or programs. I would like to acknowledge with sincere thanks the following: Ametek Straza; Applied Physics Laboratory, University of Washington; DUMAND Project; Dupont; Global Marine Development Corporation; Harbor Branch Foundation, Inc.; Heriot-Watt University; Hydro Products, Inc.; International Submarine Engineering, Inc.; Lloyds Register Information Service; Lockheed Ocean Laboratory; Marine Board, National Academy of Engineers; National Oceanic and Atmospheric Administration; Oceaneering International; Perry Oceanographics, Inc.; Remote Ocean Systems, Inc.; Scripps Institution of Oceanography; Undersea Vehicle Committee, Marine Technology Society; United States Navy, Naval Ocean Systems Center; University of Southern California; and Woods Hole Oceanographic Institution.

And, finally, I would like to thank my family, all of whom participated so actively in this book's preparation: To my wife, Nula, for her constant encouragement as well as review and editing; to my daughter, Carol, and my son, Alan, for their aid in editing and typing. Without their dedicated assistance, this book would never have been written.

Howard R. Talkington

Contents

ix

undersea
work
systems

1
Introduction

On the Thursday before Easter in 1966, a hydrogen bomb was lifted from the floor of the Mediterranean Sea a few miles from the small town of Palomares, Spain. Thus ended the operations of the greatest collection of undersea equipment ever assembled. For 81 days, the undersea depths had been probed by swimmers, divers, small and large manned submersibles, towed and self-powered unmanned vehicles, and a vast armada of surface support ships. On the day after recovery, Good Friday, a parade of participants was held to honor the hundreds of men who now had completed their part in this extensive operation. As each vehicle or ship passed by the flagship, USS Albany, it was observed by a large contingent of the world's press corps. Figure 1-1, taken by a Spanish newspaper photographer, shows the triumph of the operation, "La Bomba," with the recovery vehicle CURV I and its crew in the background aboard the USS Petrel.

The search for and ultimate recovery of the lost H-bomb demonstrated many facets of undersea work systems. First, the general location of the worksite had to be identified, a surface navigation system set up, the environmental conditions both above the surface and undersea ascertained, and a prediction facility established. Surface support ships were immediately identified and organized under a single command. Based on the initial estimates of the undersea conditions, desired search sensors were defined.

Figure 1-1   The recovered H-bomb, Palomares, Spain, April 1966. (U.S. Navy.)

These sensors were of a wide variety, ranging from the eyes of divers to cameras to acoustic side-scan sonars. Transporters for the sensors included the divers themselves and a number of manned and unmanned vehicles, all operating under a variety of navigational controls. Upon location and identification of the H-bomb, a set of tools for attachment and lift was prepared, and a vehicle was designated to transport the tools to the sea floor and effect the recovery.

A full gamut of undersea work systems was exercised during this one operation. Due to the state of the art at that time, success was achieved only by the application of brute force, that is, with large numbers of workers operating many types of equipment a long period of time. Since 1966, advances in technology have greatly increased the effectiveness and general capability of these devices. The devices and components that are referred to when we say "undersea work systems" are those described in the preceding sample operation; they are the implements that allow "work" to be accomplished under the sea, as contrasted to undersea combat systems. Work systems include sensors, navigation equipment, tools, and the transporters that carry and position them. These vary from a free swimmer, who within his or her own physical makeup provides for all the "systems" requirements, to very complex, heavily instrumented submersibles.

3 Introduction

This book was prepared as a guide book and reference for persons interested in undersea systems. In it we attempt to explain what undersea work systems are, what they do, and how they are used. We start with a definition of requirements for going into the sea. Included are tasks for commercial and academic activities as well as government agencies. We identify the environmental factors that are so crucial to the design and operation of the systems. Vehicle system concepts are described based on identified needs and constraining conditions. Trade-offs among manned, unmanned, free-swimming, and tethered systems are analyzed. Components and materials that are the building blocks of systems are described, with advances in technology highlighted and shortages in capability noted. Techniques of subcomponent fabrication, system assembly, and testing are detailed. Surface support craft, cranes, and rigging that handle the work systems and the task item as well as the requirements for the logistics at the shore support base are discussed.

There is a special section that includes descriptions, photos, and operating characteristics of representative currently operating systems. These examples have been carefully selected to provide the reader with impressions of the wide variety of systems available for use and the clever innovations of designers responding to a plethora of requirements. Some examples of operations that required particularly complicated tasks to be performed are described to show the combined applications of numbers of subsystems and components. And finally, an advance system concept is analyzed to show a particularly challenging engineering effort that combines all the parts described in the early chapters.

To be successful, the development of any undersea work system must follow a logical approach. The tasks to be performed (the mission) and the environment within which the tasks are to be performed first must be identified, followed by the formulation of a concept based on these functional inputs. A selection of components and materials may then be made based on knowledge of the state of technology. Careful fabrication and assembly must be followed by a well-planned test program. The total project must be controlled by adequate documentation both for design definition and safety of operation. Following a methodology of this type will not guarantee success, but it will certainly assist in achieving the goal.

2
Undersea Work Tasks

Any discussion on the development and operation of undersea work systems must begin with an understanding of the tasks to be accomplished. The ultimate objectives for the systems and components discussed in this book are to perform useful work in the sea. The definition of this work, and its breakdown into tasks, such as recovery of a torpedo as shown in Figure 2-1, identifies the tools, sensors, and their means of locomotion. This transportation, command, and control of the tools and sensors might be by manned submersibles, unmanned vehicles, or divers. Since economics of time and resources as well as safety are the basis of all effective operations, the proposed task needs must be thoroughly understood and system objectives clearly defined prior to the commencement of design of particular devices.

The tasks most commonly conducted within the sea fall into five categories. These are the tasks associated with (1) emergency situations, (2) commercial endeavors, (3) scientific exploration, (4) regulatory monitoring and investigations, and (5) testing.

Emergencies

Emergency situations usually involve an important time factor due to potential loss of life, objects of extreme value, or unacceptable delays in

5

Figure 2-1   Recovery of a torpedo from the sea floor. (U.S. Navy.)

crucial operations. Very often these are due to an accident causing a manned vehicle to sink to the sea floor like the PISCES III shown in Figure 2-2, or a failure of a submarine or small submersible, or to a diver's habitat from which immediate rescue is imperative. At other times, a very valuable or dangerous substance might have become lost at sea and immediate reacquisition, or outright recovery, is important. This might include such items as bombs, missiles, warheads, aircraft, ships, leaking pipes, or toxic or nuclear materials. The following types of tasks are required in order to respond to emergency situations.

Search.   Conduct a detailed search of the designated area to locate the target on the sea floor and provide position information for subsequent operations.

Inspection.   Relocate the target, and conduct a detailed inspection to verify that the detected target is truly the item in question and to ascertain its condition and detail characteristics prior to the next operation.

Recovery/Salvage.   Prepare the item for lift from the sea floor by attaching lifting lines or devices and cutting away moorings or clutter. Then apply controlled vertical lifting force to effect recovery to the ocean's surface. If the

Figure 2-2   Rescue of PISCES III. (U.S. Navy.)

item is to be transported from the scene while still in the water, such as for ships and large craft, then the rigging for tow and means to supply horizontal force may be as important as the original vertical lift.

Assembly, Modification, or Repair.   The objectives of these tasks are to conduct work on objects on the sea floor, buried beneath the sea floor, or within the sea volume; to disassemble and reassemble component parts; or to effect repairs, improvements, or alterations.

Neutralization.   Neutralization is applied to modify objects (possibly by explosive means) to render them safe for future operations, e.g., mine clearance, explosive ordnance detonation, or removal of obstructing wreckage.

Commercial Activities

Activities of commercial endeavors primarily involve (1) the exploitation of sea floor resources, (2) the harvesting of resources from within the sea, (3) communications and transportation via undersea cables and pipelines, (4) sea-based power systems, and (5) sports and recreation.

Sea Floor Resources. The exploitation of sea floor resources, primarily oil, gas, and hard minerals, requires several phases of undersea operations. During the exploration phase, the work needs are heavy in the areas of sensors, navigation, and survey-type operations. The sampling phase includes requirements for means to approach the sea floor sites and physically collect samples by such means as drilling ships, drag lines, dredges, and submersibles or unmanned vehicles with coring devices and grab samplers. The production phase includes the greatest work requirement due to the needs for submerged equipment to continuously handle large volumes of material over great periods of time. During the production phase, there are often needs for inspection of undersea structures and equipment (Fig. 2-3) and means to effect repairs in situ with minimum downtime for the

Figure 2-3   Inspection task, with helper. (Hydro Products.)

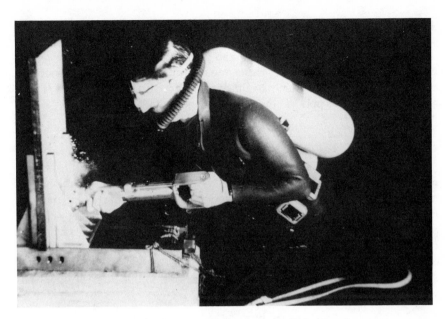

Figure 2-4   A diver operating a powered rotary tool. (U.S. Navy.)

producing units. And finally, there is the removal phase that requires that all equipment that could be a hazard or could be harmful to the environment to be removed from the site when production terminates. Each of these phases includes complex operations and contains many subtasks, as in Figure 2-4, each of which must be defined in detail prior to commencement of development of undersea work systems.

Resources within the Sea.   The harvesting of resources from within the sea includes fisheries, kelp and other plant harvesting, as well as the removal of minerals from within the seawater. Modern fisheries make use of undersea sensors to survey habitats of bottom fish, shrimp, and shellfish and to instrument deep operating trawls and nets to optimize the entrance openings. Proposals to farm kelp on subsurface floating substrates in deep water and the development of better cutting methods that protect the base plant require undersea systems engineering.

Communications and Transportation.   Cables and pipelines provide means for communication and transportation within the undersea environment. Preliminary route surveys and postinstallation inspection of cables and pipelines require acoustic and optical sensors, navigation means, and vehicles to support these sensor suites. The actual laying of the cables and pipes often requires trenching for protection from trawlers and ships' anchors. Later during their operating life, further inspection and repair are often needed, requiring sea floor bottom penetrating sonars and magnetometers to find the buried lines. Either means must be provided to uncover them, along with attachments to lift them to the surface, or work systems must be provided to perform the repairs or modification in place on the sea floor.

Sea-Based Power Systems. In this age of energy shortage, the sea is being looked to increasingly as a means for supplementing the fossil fuel reserves. Both the motion of the sea as well as its thermal differential are being studied for exploitation. There are numerous concepts for converting ocean motion into usable energy, all requiring undersea work systems for their accomplishment. The OTEC (ocean thermal energy conversion) program, discussed in Chapter 11, envisions very large volumes of cold water being transported from the depths to the surface and large sea surface platforms to support the conversion equipment, all requiring application of undersea work systems.

Sports and Recreation. Any discussion of commercial undersea activities must include sports and recreation: needs to support sport submersibles, and diving, as well as fishing. Each includes support equipment and safety and rescue capabilities.

Scientific Exploration

With 70% of the earth's surface covered by the oceans, it is easy to see why their scientific exploration is so important. The oceans control the weather, contain a multitude of resources, provide a ready means for transportation, and include areas of basic information on the formation of the earth and the growth of the continents. Many of the basic needs for scientific exploration of the oceans can and are being fulfilled by application of undersea work systems, such as the DEEPSTAR in Figure 2-5. Table 2-1, developed by the National Research Council's Marine Board panel on ocean survey needs, indicates the types and locations of measurements required to support many basic scientific investigations. The following are some specific examples.

Sea Floor Processes. Programs such as the deep sea drilling project (DSDP) are drilling and logging deep holes in selected areas of the oceans to further delineate the plate tectonics theory and to better understand the building and moving of our continents. Submersibles are being utilized to explore and document the continental margins, the mid-Atlantic Ridge, and even the

Figure 2-5   DEEPSTAR outfitted for oceanographic measurements. (U.S. Navy.)

ultimate depths of trenches, e.g., TRIESTE to the bottom of the Mariana Trench. The MANOP (magnesium nodule project) program is developing a sea floor bottom lander—a vehicle that will descend to the sea floor in depths to 5000 m (16,000 ft), remain on site to chemically measure the environment and to collect samples, and after 6 weeks to 6 months return to the surface with data helping to explain how magnesium nodule beds are formed. Many geologists are presently pursuing such work but need better undersea systems to better study the exploration of the canyons, plains, and mountains of the undersea world.

In-Volume Processes.   The dynamics and chemical characteristics of the ocean volume are just beginning to be understood in a very few carefully chosen regions. Chemical and nuclear measurements of the waters, current

Table 2-1 Needs Parameters Related to Regime and Time Interval of Measurement[a]

Parameter	Air-sea interface (+10 to −10 m)	Upper water column (−10 to −500 m)	Lower water column (> 500 m)	Bottom	Subbottom
Temperature	2, 3	2, 3	2, 6		
Surface meteorology	1, 3				
Sea-swell-surf	2, 3				
Surge	2, 3				
Currents	1, 2, 3	1, 2, 3	1, 2, 3		
Tides	1				
Ice	2, 3, 5				
Salinity	2, 3	2, 3	2, 6		
Pollutants	1, 2, 6	1, 2, 6	1, 2, 6	2, 6	
Noise	2, 6	2, 6	2, 6		
Hydrodynamic forces	2, 6	2, 6	2, 6		
Biomass	2, 3, 5, 6	2, 3, 5, 6	2, 3, 5, 6	2, 3, 5, 6	
Nutrients	2, 3, 5, 6	2, 3, 5, 6	2, 3, 5, 6	2, 3, 5, 6	
Oxygen	2, 3, 5, 6	2, 3, 5, 6	2, 3, 5, 6	2, 3, 5, 6	
Gravity					4, 6
Electrical		4, 6	4, 6	4, 6	
Magnetics					4, 6
Radiometric				2, 4, 6	2, 4, 6
Seismic					4, 6
Geothermal				2, 4, 6	2, 4, 6
Geology				4, 6	4, 6
Eng. properties				4, 6	4, 6
Phys. properties				4, 6	4, 6
Geomorphology				2, 4, 6	
Bathymetry				4, 6	
Turbidity	2, 3, 5, 6	2, 3, 5, 6	2, 3, 5, 6		
Rheology				4, 6	
Geochemistry				4, 6	4, 6

[a]The numbers in the table refer to the following remarks: 1. Continuous, 2. Periodic, 3. Synoptic, 4. One-shot, 5. Seasonal, and 6. Detail verification. *Source:* "Summary of the Proceedings of the Workshop at Airlie, Virginia, or Perspectives for Ocean Exploration and Survey Systems 1975-1985," a working document prepared for the use of the participants (1972). Courtesy of the National Research Council.

speed and direction, temperature, sound velocity and propagation, light intensity and attenuation, and magnetic aberrations are just a few of the characteristics that vary with time, depth, and location within the sea. The basic scientific phenomena must be thoroughly understood in each ocean area where useful operations are required. Undersea work systems can provide means to collect and document data to assist in this scientific endeavor.

Seismic Measurements.   The rim of the Pacific is sometimes called the "Ring of Fire" because of the large amount of volcanic activity along its shores. Along with this volcanic activity is a series of major earthquake faults. Seismic stations throughout the Pacific and other ocean areas are important to better understand the formation of earthquakes and, possibly one day, to forecast their occurrence.

Sea Life Studies.   The ocean's propensity for providing mankind a major source of food is well known. But only a minor amount of the resource that is available is actually being utilized. Undersea systems can assist in finding locales for new catches, provide more efficient means to harvest without deleting the stock, and provide more cost-competitive methods of seeding and farming the seas.

The Ocean as a Laboratory.   The oceans with their large volumes and unique characteristics may sometimes be utilized as locations for laboratory experiments that are not possible elsewhere. Several large-scale experiments are underway involving the natural processes of the sea, such as broad ocean current studies and weather modification trials. A particularly good example of use of the ocean as a laboratory involves the proposed DUMAND (deep underwater muon and neutrino detector) program. This project proposes to instrument a cubic kilometer of the sea, at a depth of about 5000 m (16,000 ft), with 23,000 optical sensors to detect and track extragalactic neutrinos (cosmic rays). This project proposes to use that cubic kilometer (10^9 metric tons) of seawater as a collector and display mechanism for determining both the direction and characteristics of incoming cosmic energy, thereby creating a neutrino astronomy telescope, and to measure and record the characteristics of the atomic particles resulting from the collisions of the neutrinos with the protons of the hydrogen nucleus in seawater molecules, thereby creating a neutrino microscope. The installation and maintenance of equipment within the sea to support such experiments as this require major efforts in the field of undersea work systems. In Chapter 10 we shall further describe the task requirements and undersea work system needs for a DUMAND-type experiment as an example of systems synthesis, from the basic definition of need to the ultimate system operation.

Regulatory Monitoring

To provide for the safety of personnel and equipment and for protection of the environment, certain government regulations have been formulated that require monitoring or investigations of activities within the sea. The following are some items that require the use of undersea work systems.

Chemical and Nuclear Dumping. Sites for the dumping of chemical, explosive, or nuclear wastes require detail surveys and monitoring. The initial survey includes the definition of the sea floor conditions, the characterization of the near floor water dynamics, and verification of the isolation of the site. After dumping occurs, routine periodic surveys (Fig. 2-6) are required to ascertain that no deleterious effects have taken place. The periodic surveys may include actual recovery of sample items for diagnostic inspection as well as water and soil samples and photographs.

Mining Leases. Sea floor mining lease agreements require environmental impact analysis that includes definitive acoustic and optical surveys, and monitoring operations to prove compliance with specific regulations.

Figure 2-6   Inspection and soil sampling near a nuclear waste disposal container. (U.S. Navy.)

Off-Shore Structures Verification.   The proliferation of offshore structures for resource exploitation has provided requirements for undersea inspection to prove their structural integrity on a periodic or event-oriented basis. This is required to ensure the safety of personnel, to prevent possible hazards to shipping, to continue the flow of the raw material without pollution, and to protect the investment in equipment. A wide range of nondestructive testing devices adapted to operation by undersea work systems is needed to fulfill these regulatory requirements.

U.S. Coast Guard Activities.   The U.S. Coast Guard is assigned missions in regard to the rescue of personnel from distressed civilian-operated sub-mersibles, recovery of contraband jettisoned at sea, and inspection of sunken ships to collect data for diagnostic investigations to prove liability as well as to provide a data base for future safer design and operating pro-cedures. In addition, the U.S. Coast Guard's missions to provide navigation aids, pollution control, and forecasting require support by equipment and sensors that function effectively in the sea.

Coastal Environmental Protection.   Local and state water resource and coastal commissions are being established to provide a means to protect the coastal environment. Particularly, the proliferation of electrical power plants (both nuclear and fossil fueled) along our coastlines is creating undersea activities in regard to construction, protection, location, and temperature differential of the cooling water intake and outfall pipelines. The near shore dynamics of erosion of sand, protection of seawalls and marinas, river outfalls, etc., are of direct interest to these local groups. These organizations are setting regulations that require measurement and monitor-ing of many undersea characteristics and activities that delineate additional needs for undersea sensors and support equipment.

Testing

A final function that establishes needs for undersea work systems is the testing and evaluation of the tools and equipment themselves as well as of other systems that operate in the undersea environment. Undersea tests require monitoring of the equipment under test with acoustic and optical sensors, the installation of the equipment at the test site, and the recovery of the equipment after the tests. The tests may be of a short-term dynamic type, such as proof of operability of a sensor in the pressure, temperature, and chemical conditions of the ocean environment, or long-term corrosion or fatigue-type testing. Some systems are so large and complex that testing in pressure tanks is inappropriate and only well-instrumented in situ ocean ranges can provide the characteristics required. Often the testing protocol requires functions that are not totally controllable, and sometimes the test object itself (e.g., submersibles, torpedoes, missiles, or deep-operating sensor packages) becomes lost, thereby requiring full-scale search and recovery capability. As shown, this function of test and evaluation may often provide the most stringent requirements on the capabilities of undersea work systems.

Bibliography

Anderson, S. H. (1975). Recreation—Marine Promise. University of Southern California Sea Grant, Los Angeles.

Booda, L. L. (1976). Marine mining faces bright economic future, *Sea Technology*, Vol. 17, No. 8, August 1976.

Booda, L. L. (1977). Storage of radioactive waste in sea fracture deeps proposed, *Sea Technology*, Vol. 18, No. 12, December 1977.

Brahtz, J. F. (1968). *Ocean Engineering, System Planning and Design*. Wiley, New York.

Busby, R. F. (1978). Underwater Inspection, Testing, Monitoring of Offshore Structures. National Oceanic and Atmospheric Administration, Office of Ocean Engineering, Rockville, Md.

Cousteau, J. Y. (1963). *The Living Sea*. Harper & Row, Pub., New York

Green, F. (1977). EPA's view of projected oil drillings on the continental shelf, *Sea Technology*, Vol. 18, No. 10, October 1977.

Griffin, O. M. (1977). Power from the ocean's thermal gradients, *Sea Technology*, Vol. 18, No. 8, August 1977.

Institute for Marine and Coastal Studies (1977). The Planning and Management of California's Coastal Resources. University of Southern California, Los Angeles.

Marine Board (1975). Mining in the Outer Continental Shelf and in the Deep Ocean. National Academy of Sciences, Washington, D.C.

National Advisory Committee on Oceans and Atmosphere (1974). Engineering in the Ocean. U.S. Government Printing Office, Washington, D.C.

Ocean Affairs Board (1979). The Continuing Quest. National Research Council, Washington, D.C.

Oceanographer of the Navy (1967). The Ocean Engineering Program of the U.S. Navy. Office of the Oceanographer, Alexandria, Va.

Oceanographer of the Navy (1967). The Ocean Science Program of the U.S. Navy. Office of the Oceanographer, Alexandria, Va.

Oceanographer of the Navy (1976). Directions for Naval Oceanography. Office of the Oceanographer, Alexandria, Va.

Rao, R. S. (1975). *The Public Order of Ocean Resources: A Critique of the Contemporary Law of the Sea*. M.I.T. Press, Cambridge, Mass.

Talkington, H. R. (1978). Underwater work systems research and development, in *Proceedings Offshore Technology Conference 1978, Houston*.

U.S. Congress (1977). Congress and the Oceans: Marine Affairs in the 99th Congress. U.S. Government Printing Office, Washington, D.C.

White, R. N. (1976). NOAA's ocean priorities—energy, environment and food, *Sea Technology*, Vol. 17, No. 1, January 1976.

3
Environmental Factors

The development and operation of undersea work systems must take into account the environmental conditions that will be encountered at the potential worksites. This is true for the submerged work areas as well as for the surface conditions that so strongly affect the launch and recovery of the undersea systems and for the station keeping of the support craft during the actual time of submerged operations.

Pressure

The primary environmental effect that must be considered is that seawater must be kept away from certain parts of the system. This requires design for the pressure effect as well as the objective of keeping internal components dry. Materials and design techniques must be carefully matched to achieve a size/weight/cost balance for producing efficient pressure-resistant housings. In Chapter 5 we shall provide additional information in this regard. With pressure increasing at about 0.50 psi for each additional foot of depth, housings for deep depth must be designed to take advantage of the compressive strengths of materials to withstand the high compressive loads applied by the pressure and to keep tensile loads to a minimum.

Sea Floor

Operations on or near the sea floor are strongly affected by near bottom currents, by the sea floor soil characteristics, and by the temperature and density (primarily salinity) of the water. To do work on the sea floor, systems must be maneuverable and be capable of holding precise position relative to the object on which the work is to be conducted. Near bottom currents tend to move the work systems about, so that it is important to design them with minimal "sail" area (low cross-section frameworks) and with adequate thruster capability to withstand the maximum forces that expected currents may produce. Currents on the sea floor in deep basin areas seldom exceed 0.05–0.10 knots, with higher currents of up to 2–4 knots in areas of shallow high tidal activity. Silty sea floors are difficult places in which to work (see Fig. 3-1), since the motions induced by the work system will cause a stirring of the silt that results in a turbidity increase within the field of view of the optical sensors. Increased turbidity due to stirring of the sea floor sediments can persist from 10 to 60 min, depending on the type of sediments and the currents. It is important to design the systems with the thrusters placed as high off the bottom as possible and to design the thrusters to direct the forces as near horizontal as can be achieved so as not to stir the silt any more than

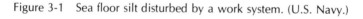

Figure 3-1   Sea floor silt disturbed by a work system. (U.S. Navy.)

is absolutely necessary. Knowledge of the sea floor characteristics is also crucial if the work tasks include digging, jetting, or backfilling into the bottom or overcoming the "breakout" force of an object being removed from the sea floor. The physical characteristics of the water near the sea floor such as temperature, density, salinity, and turbidity are important in regard to buoyancy control and the operation of the acoustic and optical sensors. These characteristics affect both the optical transmissivity, and thereby the optical sensor's effectiveness, and the speed of sound in water, thus affecting the accuracy and resolution of acoustic systems.

Ocean Volume

The conditions within the ocean volume between the surface and the worksite also affect the undersea work system. The crosscurrents and the variability of physical parameters with depth must be recognized. Very often ocean currents vary with depth, sometimes with gross changes in direction and velocity (current shears). Traversing through these currents on the way to the worksite requires accurate in-volume navigation to compensate for the horizontal excursions caused by the currents. If the system is tethered, then the tether cable will be subject to drag forces produced by the varying current force vectors. These drag forces are imparted directly to the vehicle working on the sea floor. Similarly, variations in temperature, salinity, and density of the ocean's depths will affect the buoyancy or vertical thrust requirement for diving the systems as well as the navigational and monitoring sensor systems. The stability of the electronic and electrical circuits may be upset by gross temperature variations such as 80–100°F at the surface, to 60°F near the surface, to 28°F at depth.

Chemistry and Biology

Chemical and biological conditions at the worksite can become important if the devices are to remain at depth for extended periods of time or are not properly cleaned after each undersea excursion. Careful selection of materials and the isolation of one from another are important to reduce the effects of galvanic action and the resultant corrosion (Fig. 3-2). This is due to dissimilar metals being utilized in the conducting seawater environment. The amounts of dissolved oxygen and other elements vary with depth and location within the sea, and these must be understood to predict the potential for rust or decay at specific sites. The amount of oxygen dissolved in seawater may vary from 5.1 to 6.0 ml/liter at the surface to zero at the bottom in some locations, with a concentration of 2.0–3.0 ml/liter more usual. Biofouling can occur at many different depths dependent on the physical characteristics of the individual site. Fouling can strongly affect the operability of undersea systems, particularly in the impairment of optical

Figure 3-2   A sample of corrosion effects. (U.S. Navy.)

Figure 3-3   High sea state hampers operations. (U.S. Navy.)

and acoustic active surfaces, the plugging of intakes, or the clogging of rotating surfaces.

Ocean Surface

The ocean surface is ever changing. It is this nonstatic plane, as shown in Figure 3-3, that most undersea operations must be based. The bobbing surface craft, that tends the submerged equipment, is often the most critical link in the chain of logistic support. The pitch, heave, roll, and drift of the surface support craft must be taken into account during the design of the system that will eventually operate within the sea.

The motions of the craft are caused by the natural surface environmental effects of sea state, height and direction of swells or waves, and wind. They may be reduced by the size and configuration of the ship's hull and the ship's heading relative to the winds and swells. Only craft specially designed for ultrastable operation, such as those with semisubmerged hulls (the SWATH, small waterplane area twin hull, or semisubmerged drilling rigs), will remove most of the detrimental forces that occur at the sea's surface. Usually specially designed handling equipment with motion-compensated rigging is required to match the accelerations experienced on board the designated support craft. Active or passive booms, A-frames, or hook blocks may be developed to overcome the hazardous effects of the nonstabilized seagoing platform. An additional item, often neglected, that occurs aboard the surface support craft is the ever-present salt spray. The undersea portions of the systems always have "watertight" electrical connectors. Most of the time it is just as important that the topside portions also be wired via watertight electrical connectors, since continuing salt spray penetrates the components and causes a multitude of electrical shorts.

The one constant feature involving environmental conditions is their variability. Like all weather, conditions at sea change. All operations must be scheduled carefully to occur during the optimum weather conditions but must also be planned to continue in adverse conditions. This variability applies to the undersea environment as well as that at the surface. Many undersea operations involving complex tasks or deep excursions require commitments for long periods of time for each dive. Often, even after completion of the undersea task or a decision to abort a dive has been made, 4–12 hr may be required to complete the operation. Since in many areas sea conditions can drastically shift in less than 2 hr, it can be seen that there is a basic requirement that systems must be provided that can continue to operate effectively and safely in adverse weather.

Bibliography

Bascom, W. (1964). *Waves and Beaches, the Dynamics of the Ocean Surface.* Anchor Books, Doubleday, New York.

Brahtz, J. F. (1968). *Ocean Engineering, System Planning and Design*. Wiley, New York.

Carson, R. L. (1950). *The Sea around Us*. Oxford University Press, New York.

Geyer, R. A. (1977). *Submersibles and Their Use in Oceanography and Ocean Engineering*. Elsevier, Amsterdam.

Long, E. J. (1964). *Ocean Sciences*. U.S. Naval Institute, Annapolis, Md.

Ocean Affairs Board (1979). The Continuing Quest. National Research Council, Washington, D.C.

Oceanographer of the Navy (1967). The Ocean Science Program of the U.S. Navy. Office of the Oceanographer, Alexandria, Va.

Shenton, E. H. (1968). *Exploring the Ocean Depths*. Norton, New York.

4
Vehicle Systems Concepts

In the preceding two chapters we have discussed the importance of defining the tasks to be accomplished in supporting specific undersea operations and the crucial manner in which the environmental conditions affect the equipment utilized in the operations. With an understanding of the tasks and knowledge of the expected environment, vehicle systems concepts may now be innovated. Each system must have a purpose, and this will identify the sensors and working tools required. The location of the worksite and the duration and complexity of the task will determine the means of transporting and controlling the sensors and tools.

Integrating this information on basic work requirements, a system concept can now be formulated and a decision made: to either design and develop a new system or to adapt an existing system to meet the requirements. An additional basic decision to be made is whether a manned or unmanned system can "best" perform the functions. "Best" includes consideration of time, cost, safety, and a number of other items as well as the specific functions to be accomplished. The primary component of a work system is the transporting means. Once the means of getting to the site is determined, then the other components and subsystems, discussed in Chapter 5, can be specified. The transporting means usually fall into one of the three major categories: divers, manned submersibles, or unmanned (or remotely operated) vehicles.

24

Swimmers and Divers

Humans, as swimmers or in diving suits, have been and will continue to be a major part of undersea work systems. Humans with their innate sensors, integrating brain, and manipulative arms and hands, will continue to make major contributions to the accomplishment of undersea tasks, within physiological capabilities. This includes humans as free swimmers, in scuba (self-contained underwater breathing apparatus) (as shown in Fig. 4-1), in tethered suits (as shown in Fig. 4-2), in a saturation diving mode, and in "one-atmosphere" (1-atm) diving suits. Each of the capabilities has advantages and constraints. Much has been written on the subject of manned diving systems, so little description will be repeated here. Except for saturation diving and the use of the 1-atm suit, divers are restricted to very shallow depths and relatively light work tasks. Saturation diving provides human services to depths of 610 m (2000 ft) and possibly to 920 m (3000 ft) in the future but at a high cost in equipment, mobility, and time, as required for long final decompression. The 1-atm diving suit (which might also be classified as a one-man submersible) is logistically a more mobile system than saturation diving systems and can be operated to similar depths but does not have the undersea mobility or extended depth capability of submersibles or remotely manned vehicles. Each of the types of divers' systems has useful but constrained capabilities, like all other systems, and proves to be very

Figure 4-1   A diver with underwater camera. (U.S. Navy.)

Figure 4-2   A diver in a WASP 1-atm suit. (Oceaneering International.)

useful for specific tasks. Diving systems should be considered important resources within the full spectrum of undersea work systems.

Manned Submersibles

The vehicles we call submersibles are very small submarines designed to provide a means to take one or more humans to depths within the sea beyond that obtainable by divers while retaining the comfort of a dry 1-atm environment. The early bathysphere developed by Dr. William Beebe in the 1930s was a forerunner to the sophisticated submersibles of today. The bathyscaph TRIESTE developed by Dr. Auguste Piccard was the first true free-swimming deep submersible. Built with a heavy steel bathysphere-type pressure hull, for two or three humans, it was designed similarly to the passenger balloons pioneered by Dr. Piccard. The heavy steel pressure hull is supported by a large gasoline-filled float to provide a total neutral buoyancy in seawater. Like ballooning, provision was made to vary vehicle weight and lift by carrying steel shot and by controlled release of gasoline. As in most future vehicles, diving from the surface to the sea floor is accomplished by taking on additional weight and letting gravity provide the motive force. In like manner, vertical ascent is accomplished by releasing weights and letting buoyancy provide the lift. Thus, the only power required for mobility is for horizontal excursions along the sea floor. The TRIESTE was initially designed for operations to the ultimate depths, and this was proven in 1960 when Jacque Piccard and Don Walsh descended to the record depth of 11,000 m—at the bottom of the deepest known point in the oceans, the Mariana Trench, just south of the island of Guam in the Pacific Ocean.

The first lightweight highly mobile submersible, built by Jacques Cousteau, was the sous coupe, or diving saucer (Fig. 4-3). This was developed to provide a means to supplement the diver's exploration of the sea floor by providing greater depth [to 310 m (1000 ft)] and the comfort and lack of decompression time of a dry 1-atm environment. Since then, a veritable armada of submersibles has been built and operated for a wide

Figure 4-3   Cousteau's diving saucer, sous coupe. (U.S. Navy.)

Figure 4-4   Perry PC 16 manned submersible. (Perry Oceanographics, Inc.)

variety of missions (Fig. 4-4). Much has been written on submersibles, so it will not be repeated here, except to state that for many undersea work tasks, careful selection of a submersible to match the needs of the tasks will provide the means to transport the sensors, tools, and instruments to the worksite. The manned submersible should certainly be considered one of the primary transporters of equipment for undersea work.

Unmanned Vehicles

The third type of transporter available for undersea operations is the unmanned remotely controlled vehicle. These, in turn, can be classified in three subcategories: towed, tethered, or free-swimming systems. These vehicles provide a means to transport sensors and tools to the worksite without the necessity of carrying the human operator to the site. By means of remote displays for the sensors and remote controls for the tools, these systems may be described as remotely manned systems— the operator having been moved from the worksite to the surface support platform but having retained most capabilities for integrating human intelligence into the system.

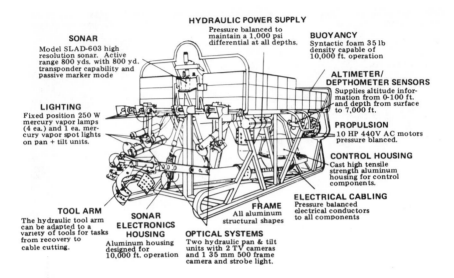

HYDRAULIC POWER SUPPLY
Pressure balanced to maintain a 1,000 psi differential at all depths.

SONAR
Model SLAD-603 high resolution sonar. Active range 800 yds. with 800 yd. transponder capability and passive marker mode

BUOYANCY
Syntactic foam 35 lb density capable of 10,000 ft. operation

ALTIMETER/ DEPTHOMETER SENSORS
Supplies altitude information from 0-100 ft. and depth from surface to 7,000 ft.

LIGHTING
Fixed position 250 W mercury vapor lamps (4 ea.) and 1 ea. mercury vapor spot lights on pan + tilt units.

PROPULSION
10 HP 440V AC motors pressure blanced.

CONTROL HOUSING
Cast high tensile strength aluminum housing for control components.

ELECTRICAL CABLING
Pressure balanced electrical conductors to all components

TOOL ARM
The hydraulic tool arm can be adapted to a variety of tools for tasks from recovery to cable cutting.

SONAR ELECTRONICS HOUSING
Aluminum housing designed for 10,000 ft. operation

FRAME
All aluminum structural shapes

OPTICAL SYSTEMS
Two hydraulic pan & tilt units with 2 TV cameras and 1 35 mm 500 frame camera and strobe light.

Figure 4-5   CURV III unmanned vehicle diagram. (U.S. Navy.)

Towed unmanned systems consist of an underwater body (usually called a FISH) that is attached to a surface vessel by a tow cable. These systems usually contain no propulsors and rely on depth control and lateral and forward motion by action of the towing line and hyrodynamic surfaces. They are usually instrumented for search or survey missions where continuous sweeps through the areas of interest are required. These devices are relatively simple and can provide large area coverage for relatively low cost and time. However, they cannot stop and take samples or do work.

Tethered unmanned systems are characterized by a subsurface vehicle constructed as a light framework, as shown in Figure 4-5, on which propulsors, sensors, and tools are installed and the whole given a slight positive buoyancy. The vehicle is tethered to a surface support platform by a cable that provides both electrical power to the vehicle and a data link between the vehicle systems and their surface monitors and controls. Usually the vehicle includes two or more horizontal thrusters that provide horizontal maneuvering control and a vertical thruster to drive down against the net positive buoyancy to provide the depth control. Acoustic and optical sensors provide the means to acquire the target worksite and/or the objects on which the work is to be performed and to monitor and control the operation of the tools or data-gathering instruments. The vehicles like that shown in Figure 4-6 are highly mobile with precise maneuverability and unlimited operational endurance due to power provided by the tether cable. Their primary

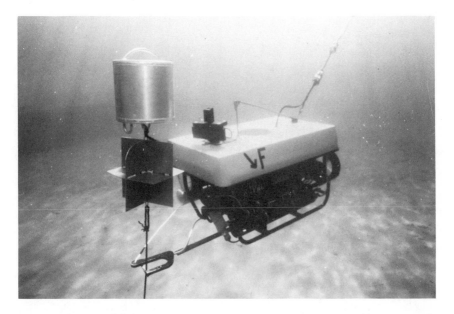

Figure 4-6   The NAVFAC SNOOPY unmanned vehicle. (U.S. Navy.)

limitations are caused by the tether that requires the surface support craft to maintain close "position keeping" for long periods of time above the work-site and the potential for becoming entangled with undersea obstructions.

Free-swimming unmanned systems are free of the tow cable or tethers that restrict the other vehicles. Systems of this type, very similar to torpedoes, have been developed to perform survey-type tasks. They require their own power supply and control system and can carry a variety of sensors. With recent advances in acoustic communications and microprocessor technology, it is now possible to build free-swimming unmanned undersea vehicles that can perform a variety of work functions (Fig. 4-7). They will be able to precisely maneuver along the sea floor, stop at a point of interest to photograph an object or collect a sample, or conduct other simple tasks. The primary limitations on these vehicles are the amount of power they can carry and the lack of fast real-time monitor and control of the work functions.

Descriptions of representative existing systems are given in Chapter 8, and examples of their applications to specific tasks are included in Chapter 9.

Selection of Approach

Three basic types of undersea systems that can perform the task of trans-porter for undersea work systems have been described. Each provides a

Figure 4-7   The NOSC free-swimmer unmanned vehicle. (U.S. Navy.)

means to extend human influence into the sea. Two take humans to the site, and the third provides a person as an operator from the surface to remotely conduct his or her functions of the selected tasks. Each of these systems have advantages and limitations. Together they provide a broad continuum of capability. But how is the "right" system selected for the specific task? Sometimes the choice is obvious, but more often it is more subtle. Different persons with differing experience will desire different means to conduct their work. The choice is often influenced by criteria other than logical engineering data or the amount of resources at hand. Let us consider some of the philosophy considered in decision making.

The initial primary decision on which undersea system to apply is whether a person is required at the undersea site. Human attempts to learn about the world in which they live have most often been conditioned by the clash between desire and economics. What a person wants to do usually far exceeds what he or she can afford to do. Columbus spent years in search of funding before he was able to finally set sail for the New World. The Apollo Program has become history; the absence of funds truncated the list of desired goals. In considering our goal of conducting work within the sea, do we need a person at the site? How does putting a person in a specific place in a system affect the goal? How does the person impact the relationship between desire and economics? These questions should be answered before any system is made the focus of time, effort, and money.

First, we must be honest with ourselves about ourselves. People have the desire to see, to know, to be there. They have egos: They wish to leave their personal mark, want others to acknowledge the achievement, and then push on. A flag could be planted on top of Mount Everest by dropping it from an aircraft, and that would indeed bring one level of satisfaction. However, to set the flag at the summit—after having scaled the heights of the icy mountain—is the supreme satisfaction, the supreme accomplishment. This is the glory of a goal personally attained. That people are searching, conquering, proud beings must be taken into account because this conviction affects the thinking of everyone who establishes goals for an undersea project, especially those who always insist that a person must be present on site. It is not being said here that this conviction is good or bad but only that it exists and must be recognized.

Beyond the desire for personal accomplishment there are other reasons people should or could be included in an undersea work or exploration system. A human is a sensing creature possessing an integrated, coordinated, active intellect. And when a person's trained intellect is part of a system, that person is able to repair, reset, adjust, adapt, and, in short, respond to the unusual situation. He or she can perform a variety of tasks because of general orientation and versatility. The free-swimming diver comes closest to exercising directly his or her senses in the ocean (primarily seeing, touching, and hearing). The person in the manned submersible, however, is sensing environment remotely, except for one sense—that of sight. In the unmanned system, all sense data are remotely perceived. Thus, the primary reason for including a person in a submersible system is to make use of his or her active, interpretive ability to see.

This seeing person is the one who is placed in a manned system, but there should be irrefutable reasons for putting a person there, because the cost is high for risking a human life in a hostile environment. There is a safety factor which makes it necessary that the system sustain and support human life. Therefore, funds must be allocated to support a person and not be directed toward accomplishing the goal. An adequate life-support system consists of more than the equipment specified strictly for life support, which in itself substantially increases the weight and complexity of the whole system and, therefore, the cost. Because manned systems are not currently powered from the surface, they require a self-contained power supply comprising special high-energy batteries and charging systems. The power supply increases the weight and volume of the system, and it generates power for only a relatively short time, thus severely limiting mission endurance—both of these facts represent a costly impact on system effectiveness. When a person is in the system, he or she must be protected from the hostile environment by a pressure hull. Since the pressure hull is usually made of steel, it becomes the largest, heaviest, and most costly part of a manned submersible. Once the manned submersible is constructed, it must undergo human-rating certification. This procedure of tests and documentation is not only costly in itself, but it imposes necessary and costly design constraints that all support components and subsystems must meet. Along with the safety factor is the anxiety factor: When a manned submersible becomes entangled in sea floor wreckage, there is a great deal of concern for the safety of those on board. However, if an unmanned system becomes entangled, that parameter of anxiety does not exist. A person in a system also complicates the already difficult problem of handling because manned systems, besides being larger and heavier, require a special fail-safe handling capability, and any accidental rough handling could result in injury or death. This handling capability also adds expense to the system. So the following questions must be considered when designing a system for undersea work or exploration. Why do we need a person in the system? Do we really require his or her presence at the worksite? Could the person be used as, or more, effectively away from the worksite (taking advantage of the longer mission duration potential, for instance)?

Experience with submersibles collecting environmental data illustrates what has been said. Most dives made use of the passenger for his or her ability to be an active observer. Yet that was not always the case. As an example, to meet some specific test objectives, a submersible had a full complement of scientific instrumentation, which included sound velocimeters, salinometers, water sampling devices, and a coring device, mounted on it. It was noted that during many of the test dives the scientist inside the submersible was so busy that he or she never looked out the viewport. Of course, the following question must be asked: Did the "observer" need to be there on a site? He used none of his or her senses to learn about the environment. Could these particular tasks have been accomplished just as well (and more safely and economically) with a remote-controlled system?

Another question is necessary: Is a person required on site in order to get the information we want and need regarding the ocean environment? Table 2-1 is a list of ocean exploration and survey parameters compiled by the National Academy of Engineering Marine Board Panel on Platforms for Ocean Exploration and Surveying at Airlie House, Virginia in February 1972. The list shows which parameters are pertinent at each of five separate levels: the air-sea interface ($+10$ to -10 m), the upper water column (-10 to -500 m), the lower water column (-500 m to bottom), ocean floor, and subbottom. This is illustrative of what scientists feel is necessary to better understand, assess, and use the marine environment and its resources. Not only are there many parameters to be measured, but they must be measured in many areas of the world before the oceans, which cover three-quarters of the earth, can be fully utilized. "Many measurements in many areas" is the desired goal, but once again economics affects accomplishment. It was the conclusion of the Airlie House panel that buoy systems and unmanned systems should be used whenever possible because they would enable scientists to get the maximum amount of information for their dollars. This would avoid the expense of using a manned system when the only responsibility of those on board is to ferry the instrumentation to the appropriate level for gathering data. When a person is put into a system, there must be a specific, necessary purpose for having him or her there, and he or she must achieve that purpose.

Some conclusions can be drawn, having come this far. It is recognized that, to meet the challenge of making a thorough and effective use of the marine environment and its resources, a full complement of manned and unmanned systems will be required. When a person's senses are required at the worksite in order to properly accomplish the task, the use of a manned system is justified. Unmanned systems are particularly suited to a large number of undersea work and exploration tasks for at least six reasons: relative economy of development in time and equipment costs when compared with manned systems, unlimited operational endurance on site by virtue of the cable link to the surface, surface control and coordination of project efforts (avoids clash of operational philosophies: He or she who is on the surface is in command), ability to perform in hazardous areas without endangering personnel, ability to change or modify all system components to meet individual tasks or range needs without affecting system safety or certification status, and ease of changing crews without any disruption to the mission (people simply leave their places at the control consoles, and immediately their replacements are there to take over). In addition, because these systems are usually smaller and light, as well as not containing a human passenger, the handling problem is significantly reduced.

Bibliography

Berghage, T. E. (1978). Man at high pressure: A review of the past, a look at the present, and a projection into the future, *The Marine Technology Society Journal,* Vol. 12, No. 5.

Chew, J. I., and Johnston, J. R. (1979). The Use of Unmanned Remote Controlled Vehicles for Offshore Inspection and Work Tasks. SPE 7769, presented at the Society of Petroleum Engineers Conference, 25–29 March 1979. Society of Petroleum Engineers, Dallas.

Cousteau, J. Y. (1963). *The Living Sea.* Harper & Row, Pub., New York.

Elliott, B. (1976). Diver's mixed bag of tools amazingly versatile, *Sea Technology,* Vol. 17, No. 4, April 1976.

34

Geyer, R. A. (1977). *Submersibles and Their Use in Oceanography and Ocean Engineering.* Elsevier, Amsterdam.

Goodfellow, R. (1977). *Underwater Engineering.* Petroleum Publishing Co., Tulsa.

Gray, W. E., and Fridge, D. S. (1978). How to select diving systems in offshore applications, *Ocean Industry,* Vol. 13, No. 4, April 1978.

Hales, R. (1978). *LR in Hydrospace.* Lloyd's Register Information Service, London.

Mulcahy, M. (1977). Commercial diving outlook mostly bright for 1978, *Sea Technology,* Vol. 18, No. 12, December 1977.

Myers, M. (1969). *Handbook of Ocean and Underwater Engineering.* McGraw-Hill, New York.

Oceanographer of the Navy (1976). Directions for Naval Oceanography. Office of the Oceanographer, Alexandria, Va.

Partridge, D. W. (1979). The underwater initiative, progressive replacement of man underwater, *Offshore Research Focus,* Vol. 13, June 1979.

Talkington, H. R. (1973). Why Man? NUC TN 953. Naval Oceans Systems Center, San Diego.

Vadus, J. R. (1976). International Status and Utilization of Undersea Vehicles 1976. National Oceanic and Atmospheric Administration, U.S. Department of Commerce, Rockville, Md.

5
Vehicle Materials and Components

Vehicle systems designed for undersea work are actually the assembly of a large number of subsystems and components, often in modular form to provide for reassembly into several formats to allow optimization for particular mission needs. Advancing technology provides opportunities to achieve new capabilities through application of such fields as materials, solid-state electronics, signal processing, microprocessors, chemistry, acoustics, and many other basic sciences. Following are some items to watch that are having impact on the development of new vehicle systems and show considerable promise for even greater benefits in the future.

Materials

A veritable technological explosion is taking place in electrical and electronic materials and their applications to components. The continuing development of solid-state devices, from transistors and diodes to large-scale integration (LSI) and very large-scale integration (VLSI) circuitry, has opened whole new arenas for undersea application. These include microprocessors, multiplex systems, all manner of control and monitoring components, laser illumination, and power conversion and control, all of which may be made pressure-tolerant and can be installed in lightweight, oil-filled,

Table 5-1 Performance Capabilities of Various Batteries [at a specific power of 22 W/kg (10 W/lb)]

Batteries	Specific energy	
	W hr/lb	W hr/kg
Alkal (MnO_2)	6	12
Lead-acid	8	16
Nickel-cadmium	20	40
Nickel-zinc	30	60
Silver-zinc	60	120
Zinc-air	75	150
Lithium organic	130	260
Lithium-chloride	200	400
Lithium-sulfide	200	400
Lithium inorganic	350	700

pressure-compensated containers for operations to all depths in the sea. In a supportive role for electrical application is the development of the electro-chemistry, packaging, and handling techniques required to provide safe high-energy-density batteries.

Research and development are underway to increase the energy density of batteries and to provide greater power for longer duration to increase the effectiveness of equipment for undersea missions. Table 5-1 provides data on the relative amounts of energy per weight for a number of battery configurations. As the energy density increases, so does the possibility of it's uncontrolled release (explosions). The most favorable battery, on an energy per weight basis, is the lithium inorganic, with a storage capacity of up to 350 W hr/lb or about 700 W hr/kg. This is more than 40 times the capability of lead-acid types. Recent research has brought breakthroughs in the safe packaging of lithium inorganic systems such that safety-certified batteries large enough to power major undersea systems may soon be available.

Aluminum, titanium, and high-strength, lightweight steel alloys are fairly well-developed materials and are currently in extensive use in modern undersea systems. All materials considered for application within the sea must have resistance to the corrosive effects of salt water. Careful analysis must be made of their stress-corrosion and corrosion-fatigue resistance characteristics. If the structure involved is subject to repeated stress, then basic fatigue failure must be avoided by careful design. Much has been written on the common metals as they are utilized in the undersea environment. This chapter is not intended as a handbook, but the values in Table 5-2 may be helpful in considering the types of materials available for

Table 5-2   Characteristics of Selected Metals

Material	Density (lb/ft^3)	Yield strength (psi X 10^3)	Ultimate strength (psi X 10^3)	Modulus of elasticity (psi X 10^6)
Steel				
HY 80	484	80	100	30
HY 140	484	140	180	30
4340	484	220	270	30
Stainless (301)	484	50	110	28
Monel	556	30	75	26
Naval brass	534	58	70	15
Aluminum				
2424-T4	173	40	62	10.6
7075-T6	173	70	80	10.5
6061-T6	173	35	42	10.1
Titanium				
6A1-4V (An)	276	120	130	15.5
Lead	710	—	2	2

application to particular structures. A more detailed engineering text should be consulted for specific design information. The continuing development of plastics, glass, and synthetic fibers, however, appears to be making possible many advances in the area of high strength retention coupled with drastic weight reduction.

A current synthetic aramid fiber, duPont's KEVLAR-49, shows great promise as a reinforcing component for replacing glass in GRP (glass-reinforced plastic) used for pressure housings. It provides a 33% reduction in volume and a 50% reduction in weight for equal strength. The high tensile strength (200,000 psi) and modulus of elasticity (12 million psi) of KEVLAR-49 makes it an ideal material with which to replace steel as the strength member in composite undersea cables, as shown in Figure 5-1.

A series of deep-sea electromechanical cables has been developed that are characterized by high strength and light weight in water. The strength member for these cables is KEVLAR-49, which combines usable tensile strength comparable to that of steel with an in-water weight about one-twelfth that of steel. The composite cable, when used as a deep-sea tether, has 5–10 times the strength/self-weight capability of conventional steel-armored cable. High strength to weight is important in a number of ways. First, for very deep operations requiring long cables, the weight of the cable itself does not take up most of the allowable load, as sometimes happens with steel cables. Second, the higher strength allows for a smaller

Figure 5-1 The aramid fiber KEVLAR-49 being drawn into a cable. (U.S. Navy.)

cross section, thereby reducing sea current drag on the cable as well as reducing the size of the surface storage reel and handling rigging. Third, with the addition of a small cross-sectional volume of buoyancy by filler strands, the overall cable may be made buoyant for use as vehicle tethers. One of the early objections to the use of KEVLAR-49 was its high cost, which was approximately $50/lb when processed into a form analogous to cylindrical steel wires. More recent work has shown that this material can be formed into cables at a material cost of $8.50/lb. (This corresponds to a cost of about $1.50/lb for cabling steels that have the same strength.) Little or no penalty in strength is paid, although some reduction in flexure lifetime has been experienced. This material has direct application to such undersea systems as pressure hulls, hydrodynamic fairings, structural members, and cabling.

The development of optical fibers that can be drawn in long, high-strength lengths offers advances that are directly applicable to undersea vehicle tethers, namely very high signal bandwidth, low volume and weight, low signal attenuation, and freedom from EMI (electromagnetic interference) and cable cross talk. A typical 0.12-mm- (0.005-in.-) diameter optical fiber can provide a usable bandwidth of at least 50 MHz over a length of more than 7600 m (25,000 ft), which is sufficient to support a sophisticated tethered system operating at abyssal depths. For comparison, as shown in

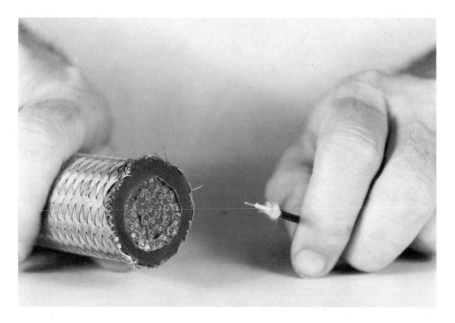

Figure 5-2   Comparative sizes of fiber optic and regular electrical cables. (U.S. Navy.)

Figure 5-2, a conventional 21.6-mm- (0.9-in.-) diameter coaxial cable provides a bandwidth of about 13 MHz over the same cable length. For certain applications, miniature optomechanical strands can be used as the entire tether cable or can be assembled as a conductor element into larger cables of arbitrary size, capacity, and complexity.

Underwater panoramic visibility is of vital importance to undersea work systems for exploration, research, rescue, salvage, and ocean engineering operations. Such panoramic visibility improves operating safety, convenience, and efficiency in the undersea environment. Acrylic plastic has been used to construct many-sized windows, some examples of which are shown in Figure 5-3, and large panoramic windows and transparent hulls for manned submersibles. Such structural components currently have operational depth capabilities of 610 m (2000 ft). Fabrication technology for 2-m- (78-in.-) diameter acrylic plastic hemispheres is currently being developed that will increase the service depth to 920 m (3000 ft). Acrylic has also been used for small windows for very deep depths. The window in the TRIESTE, which dove to the ultimate depths, is 10 cm (4 in.) in diameter at the small face of a truncated cone 12 cm (5 in.) thick and 30 cm (12 in.) across at the outside diameter. When placed in a pressure hull opening with the large diameter on the high-pressure side, the loading is taken out in

Figure 5-3   Transparent acrylic windows. (U.S. Navy.)

wedging the sloped sides against corresponding sloped sides of the pressure hull penetration. Windows for optical viewing systems in unmanned vehicles provide abyssal depth capability by utilizing glass-ceramic fabrication. Spherical, 20-cm- (8-in.-) diameter windows successfully perform at 11,000 m (36,000 ft) withstanding the pressure of the greatest known ocean depth.

Undersea vehicles must keep proper trim and remain near neutral buoyancy throughout their operating environment. Early vehicles made use of fluids (e.g., gasoline) for buoyancy and also used fixed- or variable-buoyancy tanks. The current primary means to provide buoyancy is to install syntactic foam. Unlike fluids, syntactic foam is not affected by changes in pressure or temperature and, when properly manufactured, will not absorb appreciable amounts of water, even at depths to 6100 m (20,000 ft). Syntactic foam is essentially a composite mixture of tiny hollow glass spheres in an epoxy matrix. The density is governed by the ratio of epoxy to glass spheres. The initial foams had a density of about 480 kg/m³ (30 lb/ft³) for operations to 610-m (2000-ft) depths. The higher-strength foams initially were 580-kg/m³ (36 lb/ft³) for operating depths to 6100 m (20,000 ft). Several industries have been working on manufacturing techniques, and densities are falling rapidly, with 480-kg/m³ (30-lb/ft³) foam now available for deep applications and foams as light as 320 kg/m³ (20 lb/ft³) for medium depths. This is a field to watch closely, for advances are being announced continually.

With the advent of solid-state electronic components, a major improvement in the packaging of undersea electronic systems was made possible. The basic characteristic of pressure-tolerant electronics (PTE) (i.e., the electronics are not protected from the depth pressure) describes its real advantages. Many solid-state electronic components are, as their designation implies, very small pieces of solid crystals which, by themselves, will not respond to application of external pressure. Other very small components are made up of several parts potted in a hard substance that also resists external pressure. Many long-term pressure testing programs have been conducted on large quantities of components to certify that they do not change characteristics when subject to pressure. PTE systems are fabricated on circuit boards just as for any other application, the only difference being that a nonconducting oil is used to fill the equipment housing and a pressure-equalizing diaphragm is provided such that the internal pressure of the housing is always kept equal to the external sea pressure. This frees the designer from constraints imposed by pressure vessels; PTE systems use liquid-filled, pressure-equalized containers which provide almost unlimited freedom in choice of container size, shape, and materials. Since the inside and outside of the container experience no pressure difference, there is no need for heavy containers or high-pressure penetrators and seals. In addition to offering the advantages of few container restraints, such systems can, or will, (1) provide control of package buoyancy, (2) eliminate the potential for catastrophic pressure seal and penetrator failures, (3) provide a low thermal resistance path to the ocean, and (4) permit the design of flexible, inexpensive electronic systems capable of operation at any depth. A large number of electronic devices and components have been tested and found adequate for PTE application; many amplifiers, signal processing devices, and sonar subcomponents have been built, and a complete television camera has been modified with selected PTE parts so that it can be taken to any depth without a heavy pressure case. Figure 5-4 shows an example of PTE components applied to the electronic monitor and control system for a manipulator and tool system.

Sensors

Optical, acoustic, and magnetic sensors contribute directly to the achievement of undersea work systems. They provide the means to find the worksite, provide for inspection and documentation of the characteristics of the

Figure 5-4 The pressure-tolerant electronic (PTE) system for the work system package (WSP). (U.S. Navy.)

site, and provide the means to monitor and control the working tools during operations. Commercial television, cinema, and still cameras have been adapted successfully for use in the undersea environment. The range of vision with optical equipment varies greatly with water conditions. In the deep-sea basins where water clarity is very good, visibility to distances of 15–30 m (50–100 ft) are common. But in coastal areas where turbidity is high, ranges of 1.5–6 m (5–20 ft) are normal, with some areas so bad that you literally cannot see your hand before your face. A number of projects have attacked the problem of backscatter due to turbidity by such techniques as separating the light source a distance away from the receiver or range-gating flash illumination similar to radar range-gating techniques. The newest technology is being applied to reduce the illumination requirements by application of very sensitive vidicons and intensifier tubes for "low-light-level" television cameras. In addition, extensive development has been applied to optimize the design of underwater lights that project illumination in the optical frequencies best suited for transmission through seawater (in blue-green), while minimizing those frequencies absorbed by the sea. In this manner, a best conversion efficiency from electrical power to optical radiation is achieved, thereby minimizing the power budget for lighting.

Prior to acquiring a target at a worksite by optical means, the approach by an undersea work vehicle is usually governed by active sonar. There are several good commercial medium-range high-resolution sonars packaged for use on undersea vehicles. These sonars provide ranges of about 30–100 m (100–300 ft) with resolutions of 0.15–0.6 m (0.5 to 2 ft). The currently available units are constructed in a volume of about 0.35 m³ (1.5 ft³) and weigh about 14–23 kg (30–50 lb). While the range and resolution of these systems are adequate for most undersea operations, new technology in solid-state electronic components applied in a pressure-tolerant electronic manner, combined with advanced signal processing, can provide a great reduction in size, weight, and power consumption. An experimental "minisonar" has been demonstrated that provides the same basic parameters as the current systems but is only 0.08 × 0.2 × 0.2 m (3 × 6 × 6 in.) and weighs only 1.4 kg (3 lb). Small, lightweight sonars of this type should soon be available on the commercial market.

Recent technological developments in laser research have made possible the development of a concept of the real-time optical mapping system (ROMS) shown in Figure 5-5, which combines the qualities of high optical

Figure 5-5   The laboratory model of the real-time optical mapping system (ROMS). (U.S. Navy.)

resolution, a large swath width, and a real-time optical picture of the ocean bottom for fast search and mapping of bottom terrain. It thus bridges the gap between existing acoustic systems, which offer long-range and real-time operation but are limited by low resolution, and photographic systems, which offer high resolution but are not capable of real-time operation or large swath widths. A concept demonstration model of ROMS has been built, and shows promise, but commercial versions have not yet been developed. ROMS' performance is based on a pair of rotating, three-faced mirrors mounted on a single shaft. An argon laser beam is focused onto the mirrors on one end of the rotating shaft. The rotation of the mirrors causes the beam to sweep a 120° arc along the sea floor. The energy reflected from objects within the field illuminated by the laser beam is collected by the mirrors on the other end of the rotating shaft and transmitted through optical filters to a photomultiplier tube. The output of the photomultiplier tube is electronically processed and transmitted to the system display on the surface ship. There the data are displayed on a cathode-ray tube as a two-dimensional map and are recorded on a paper recorder for postrun analysis. The operator can control the display and adjust its contrast or zoom in on an object of interest. The demonstration hardware provides a swath width of 122 m (400 ft) when operated at an altitude of 37 m (120 ft) above the sea floor, with a resolution element size of 8 cm (3 in.). Higher resolutions but smaller swath widths are obtained by lowering the operating altitude. A 2.6-m/sec (5-knot) speed of advance provides a search rate of 0.2 square nautical mile/hr.

Pressure-tolerant, miniaturized electroacoustical solid-state components provide the basic equipment for the U.S. Navy's acoustic imaging project, which will improve the range of underwater visibility, particularly in turbid water. The general objective is to develop and demonstrate acoustic imaging technology for underwater search, recovery, classification, manipulation, and inspection aboard manned and unmanned submersibles to depths of 3660 m (12,000 ft). The program has focused on the development of a holographic (lensless) system. The acoustic imaging system (AIS) was designed to achieve a recognizable image of a beer can in turbid water at ranges of 8 m (25 ft) anywhere within the 0.2-radi (11° by 11°) field of view. Larger objects can be seen at ranges up to 46 m (150 ft). Photographs are taken at the rate of one every 2 sec, with a future capability of 15/sec. The system consists of two assemblies: (1) an underwater unit, shown in Figure 5-6, that has an acoustic projector, receiving hydrophone array, and processing electronics, and (2) a rack of control electronics that holds the control panels, minicomputer image reconstructor, and displays. The acoustic projector sends high-frequency (642-kHz) sound into the water. Underwater objects reflect this sound in sound patterns that conform to the shape of the object. The acoustic detector (48 by 96 elements) in an 0.6-m (2-ft) square senses, processes, and stores the sound pattern as an acoustic

Figure 5-6   The transmitter receiver unit for the acoustic imaging system. (U.S. Navy.)

hologram, which is then digitized and transferred to the holographic reconstructor, a digital minicomputer. The minicomputer processes the hologram to form an image which is then displayed on a screen.

Slow-scan television is undergoing extensive testing because it shows promise of providing real-time video information from underwater vehicles by means of acoustic transmission (no cable necessary). Most sensors currently used in underwater inspection, observation, and documentation either are non-real-time or require a cable to transmit real-time information to their surface support craft. The availability of already installed underwater telephones (UQCs) and low-cost, off-the-shelf scan converters (originally designed for the amateur radio market) is a major advantage. Two at-sea experiments have been conducted between submersibles and surface support vessels. Twenty-six transmissions have been completed at vertical offsets ranging from 305 to 1220 m. Straza ATM 504A UQCs were used to transmit and receive the acoustic data, and Robot model 400 scan converters were used to convert between fast- and slow-scan formats. Most received pictures showed some degree of line jitter or graininess. Analysis has revealed that these defects are the result of multipath scattering from the surface and bottom boundaries. Detailed examination of the acoustic geometry indicated that these boundary effects can be minimized by maintaining a more nearly vertical orientation. These experiments should be watched for potential use in future operations.

The head-coupled television (HCTV) and sonar system was originally built to evaluate and demonstrate the degree of "operator presence" which could be obtained with such a system. The operator, sitting in the control room on a surface ship wearing specialized equipment, simultaneously views a TV monitor presentation and hears an audio signal containing information from the sonar return signal from the direction in which the camera is pointed. The operator is presented with all the relative visual and proprioceptive information that he or she would receive if physically present at the underwater camera. The remote pan-and-tilt is positioned by an electrohydraulic position feedback system. This system causes the camera to be pointed in the direction in which the operator is pointing his or her head. By using this sytem, the operator not only has his or her hands free for other tasks but obtains a feeling of being present in the environment. HCTV systems have been incorporated into the SCAT and RUWS unmanned vehicles and have successfully met expectations for improved operator performance.

Display and control consoles and individual sensor displays, such as shown in Figures 5-7 and 5-8, must be carefully designed to present their data to the operators in the most easily recognized and useful way. Basic research is being performed to improve the efficiency of remote vehicle operators. The major focus of this task is to conduct research on and identify the key variables affecting remote vehicle operator performance. The range of research includes studies of display system parameters and task demands encountered by the remote vehicle operator and the manipulator operator. Three general manipulator tasks have been selected for detailed examination. An investigation of the operator's visual task requirements is underway, and the perceptual and motor demands for the performance of these tasks are being studied. An experimental laboratory technique has been developed to simulate the degraded underwater visibility conditions which occur as a result of the backscattering of light. Current studies are being conducted to assess manipulator operator performance under various levels of degraded visibility (clear, moderate, poor) using a conventional TV display compared to recently developed stereo displays. An analysis of the interaction of the perceptual, learning, and task factors which contribute to per-

Figure 5-7   The monitor and control console for the remote unmanned work system (RUWS).

formance will be made. Findings will be organized so as to provide human engineering guidelines for the design of displays used in remotely operated undersea vehicle and work systems.

Because of the rapid expansion of offshore resource development and the attendant offshore structures, a technology push has developed in the undersea application of nondestructive testing to support regulated inspection. This requires applying the same basic operating principles used by currently available dry-land test instrumentation but adapting the packaging for best size, shape, power consumption, local and remote readout, and waterproofing. These include devices operated by divers, or from manned or unmanned vehicles, that will perform magnetic particle inspection, radiography, ultrasonic thickness and flaw detection, and corrosion potential measurements. Optical systems such as television, film cameras, scanners, and their illuminators also play important parts in this function.

The interconnection of the sensors to the control and monitor components and vehicle power distribution system requires electrical cabling and connectors. In early development of undersea work systems, a major

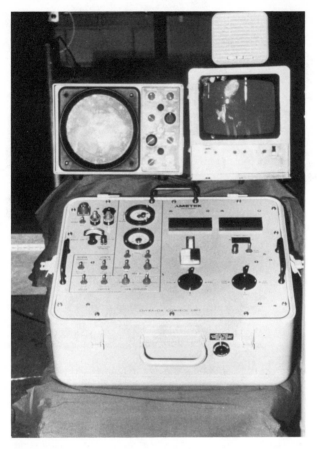

Figure 5-8 The portable monitor and control system for the Straza SCORPIO unmanned vehicle system. (Ametak Straza.)

recurring problem was in leakage and subsequent shorting of electrical systems due to failures in the cabling and connectors. Many of these failures were due to the attempt to keep the wires and connector pins dry, and at 1 atm of pressure, regardless of depth of operation. Several types of strong, heavy, expensive connectors have been developed that show a fairly high reliability and are now in regular use. However, there is a second way to attack the leakage problem: that is, to make the electrical system *pressure tolerant,* just like the PTE systems already described. To accomplish this, the individual wires required for interconnections are placed in plastic tubing; the tubing is oil-filled and sealed, allowing sea pressure to "squeeze" the oil-filled tubes, thereby keeping the internal (oil) pressure equal to the external (sea) pressure, with no differential to initiate leakage. Similarly, the connectors are provided with a small quick-acting relief valve in the center of the electrical pin insert, so that when the connectors are connected, the valve opens and allows the oil from the cable to fill the small interspace within the connector housing, thereby making it a part of the pressure-equalized system. Since these connectors themselves do not need to resist the high pressure of deep-sea operations, they may be fabricated at less expense, usually using injection-molded plastic parts. Several good, safe, nonflammable oils are now available that have the nonconductive characteristics required for immersion of operating electrical systems. The concept of pressure-equalizing components, rather than fighting the pressure of the deep sea, can produce a savings in cost, weight, and volume for many applications.

Navigation

The navigation subsystems are a most important part of undersea work systems, since they provide the means of finding a precise location and a means of returning to the same site on repeated excursions. The type of navigation applied for a particular excursion depends on the mission and the environment. It may require only a simple magnetic compass or a complex combination of acoustic devices and gyroscopes. The following are the primary types of systems in use today.

A wide variety of compasses packaged for undersea operation is available from commercial activities. These vary from relatively inexpensive magnetic compasses to sophisticated microprocessor-controlled gyrocompasses. Manufacturers' catalogs give the detailed specification, and it is just a matter of selecting the system that best meets the mission needs at the lowest penalty of cost, weight, volume, and power usage. Often compasses are complemented with acoustic doppler navigators to record the cross-current effects on a vehicle that are not recorded by compasses. Acoustic doppler navigators measure the relative velocity and direction of the vehicle with the sea floor by projecting an acoustic pulse and measuring the *dopper shift* of it's return, that is, the change in frequency of the reflected sound due to motion. By measuring and integrating over time, this relative velocity and direction will provide a record of the vehicle's travels.

In addition to compasses and doppler navigators, vehicle-borne navigation equipment includes means to measure depth and height off the bottom and a forward-looking obstacle-avoidance device. The obstacle-avoidance requirement is usually met by the sonar used as a sensor for conducting work, and this type of system was described in the preceding sensor section. The height and depth sensors (altimeter and depthometer) are usually high-frequency acoustic devices that operate like a ship's fathometer, one projecting downward and one upward. As a backup to the depthometer, or sometimes as a requirement, a precise pressure transducer can be utilized for depth measurement. The altimeter and depthometer as well as the heading indicator (compass) are often integrated into an automatic control system to provide constant values of height, depth, or heading to simplify the operation of the vehicles. For special applications, such as undersea pipeline inspection, magnetometers that accurately sense the direction to large ferrous objects (such as the pipe) can be utilized as part of an automatic navigation system or as a means to initially find the pipeline. The magnetic sensor is particularly crucial if portions of the pipeline are buried.

Instrumentation external to the vehicle is often required to monitor its track during a search phase of an operation and to assist in directing it back to a precise location on later excursions. External systems can be divided between the undersea portions and the broader area above-the-surface systems. Underwater navigation systems are mostly acoustic in nature. The simplest is use of a sonar fixed to a surface support ship. The sonar in an active (pinging) mode may be used to track the vehicle (usually with a corner reflector) to get slant range and bearing that, when coupled with depth information from the vehicle, will give a fairly good short-range plot of location during operations. In a passive mode (listening only), a ship-mounted sonar can monitor the bearing of a vehicle with an acoustic beacon and obtain a general idea of its location. Both passive and active sonar plots are dependent on precise data on ship's position and heading, and considerable errors result from ship's drift. A second and more accurate means of recording the track of an undersea vehicle from a support ship is to install passive hydrophones on the four corners of the ship to give a series of acoustic receivers with wide enough baseline between receivers to measure time difference of arrival of acoustic pulses generated at the vehicle. Three, or often four for redundancy, receivers in a horizontal plane plus one offset in the vertical plane can provide data sufficient to prepare continuous underwater tracks of one to four targets at a time without the need to mechanically steer a beam as in the operation of the sonar. This system, known as a short-baseline acoustic system, tracks well but has the disadvantage of being dependent on the ship with its errors due to pitch, roll, and drift in position and heading as well as requiring long acoustic paths from the primary areas of interest near the sea floor. The more complex sea-floor-mounted long-baseline acoustic tracking systems provide tracking by vehicle-initiated interrogation of acoustic receiver/retransmitter devices (transponders) placed on the sea floor at distances from 100 to 1000 m (300–3000 ft) apart. These systems are not subject to the disadvantages of the ship-borne systems noted above and can instrument larger areas with near equivalent precision. Their primary disadvantages are the cost for the deep operating transponders with reliable release devices and the lack of easy portability. The transponders must be recovered and reinstalled for each new area of interest, whereas ship-borne systems move with the ship.

Above-surface navigation is accomplished primarily by electronic (radio frequency) systems, such as LORAN, DECCA, LORAC, and satellite navigation systems. These are used to position the surface support ships in relative positions to the undersea operations and as a reference to hold position on the surface during undersea excursions. Precise surface positioning is especially important for cable-controlled vehicle operations in order to prevent the potentially drifting support ship from pulling the working vehicle away from its task.

Tools

For routine undersea operations, two-function claws of various sizes and shapes, cutters, and simple toggle bolts are sufficient for most work tasks. For certain of the more dexterous tasks, multifunction manipulators and specialized tools are necessary. These may vary from a specially shaped and sized wrench to open a valve or turn a bolt to an automatic pipe welding machine. For undersea work, as in automated production lines in industry, certain basic tools and manipulative devices are required that may be used as the basis for complex tasks. The following describes some types of successful undersea manipulators and the special tools adapted for them.

A manipulator must be mechanically well designed for performing the required tasks in the marine environment, and it must be integrated with controls and displays so that the operator can perform coordinated, accurate motions. Anyone with experience in remote work systems develops opinions on how to design a manipulator to optimize the capabilities of the operator through the man-machine interface, but these opinions must be reconciled with the experience of others, i.e., the human factor researchers and the operators.

The optimum manipulator and control system varies with the task. The capabilities of operators also vary, and their preferences are often a function of their experience with particular types of manipulators, controls, displays, and tasks. However, experience has led to a general awareness of certain trade-offs. For example, for tasks requiring precise positioning, rate-control devices are more accurate, whereas for general reaching and grasping, where coordination is more important than precision, master-slave manipulators are much faster. In rate-control manipulators, position feedback is purely visual, whereas for master-slave manipulators, even with computer-generated displays, there is also a natural feeling of position. Two types of master-slave controls have been used: harness and terminus control. A harness straps onto, or in some way attaches to, the arm of the operator; the terminus control is held only at the hand or terminus. They operate in the same way: The manipulator (slave) is driven to conform to the configuration and position of the control (master). The harness control may be most valu-

Figure 5-9 Manipulators and tools for the remote unmanned work system (RUWS). (U.S. Navy.)

able for use with anthropomorphic manipulators, especially those with a redundant function for elbow position. Terminus control, much more common in hot-cell nuclear work, generally allows more operator freedom and a greater range of motion and does not require an anthropomorphic manipulator.

For manipulators, such as those on the RUWS (Fig. 5-9) and work systems package (WSP; Fig. 5-10), it is anticipated that tasks requiring force feedback will occur. Examples are drilling and tapping operations where too much force or misdirected force might result in a broken tool. Of course, wherever possible, tool drive, feed, and alignment should be automatic functions of the tool itself and not of the manipulator. Unfortunately, this is not always possible. Another situation in which force sensing could be important occurs when the manipulator unexpectedly comes in contact with the work task or the vehicle. Another difficulty that the operator encounters is in maintaining a sense of orientation. Orientation and station-point feedback are provided by two methods: fixed camera and monitor or head-coupled television (the latter method should incorporate head-following translation, if possible). Head-coupled television also alleviates the problem of limited field of view, since a sweep of the head allows the operator to

Figure 5-10   The work system package (WSP) mounted on the pontoon implace-
ment vehicle (PIV). (U.S. Navy.)

encompass visually as much of the remote environment as desired, and the
spatial relationship of objects not simultaneously visible in the camera's
field of view is instinctively retained.

It must be cautioned that the best general-purpose manipulator for
underwater work is not necessarily the most sophisticated or complex. Cost,
reliability, maintainability, and the ability of the trained operator to work
within limitations must also be weighed in deciding whether to incorporate
seemingly desirable features.

An example of integration of manipulators and tools is found in the
recently completed work systems package (WSP) shown in Figure 5-10,
developed as part of the deep ocean technology program. The WSP is
comprised of manipulators and a variety of hydraulic tools that are integrated to accomplish tasks to ocean depths of 6100 m (20,000 ft). The
system can be readily adapted to the manned submersibles—ALVIN, SEACLIFF,
and TURTLE—and the robot vehicles—CURV III and RUWS—to extend their
work capabilities. In addition, it can be positioned and controlled by divers

or operated from a surface support ship. The system was designed to perform a complete work operation on the sea floor without resurfacing for tool interchange. Potential tasks include recovery, construction, installation, and repair operations. Low-light-level television cameras with quartz-iodide floodlights augment the operator's vision.

The skeletal structure of the WSP is a simple tubular network, fabricated from 5086-alloy aluminum. Its configuration is the result of spatially arranging all major system components to meet the aforementioned requirements and then connecting them with a single strongback. The problem of use with various submersibles was solved by providing an interface plate between the vehicle and WSP. The interface plate is mounted to the parent vehicle by a single 2.5-cm-diameter bolt (1 inch) that can be severed by either of two explosively actuated bolt cutters, thereby satisfying the requirement for a single-point jettison capability with redundancy.

It was necessary to reduce the underwater weight of the WSP to make it compatible with the trim capacities of each parent submersible. Blocks of syntactic foam with a density of 35 lb/ft^3 were shaped and mounted on the package and skid structure. The foam was positioned to avoid interference with work functions while providing good stability characteristics to the host vehicle.

Mounted on each end of the main cross tube are two simple manipulator or "grabber" arms which can secure and hold a workpiece for stability or assist the dexterous manipulator work arm. They are hydraulically actuated and can perform six rate-controlled functions including a 61-cm (24-in.) linear extension. Lift capacity is 113 kg (250 lb) at a 3-m (9-ft) extension, and the grip force is 227 kg (500 lb).

The dexterous work manipulator is a seven-function, hydraulically actuated, rate-controlled arm mounted above and to starboard of center. This position, in relation to the operator's normal viewing position above center and behind the package, is analogous to the relative positions of the right arm and eye of a human; it thus provides some anthropomorphic familiarity to the operator. Lift capacity of the manipulator is 45 kg (100 lb) with the arms fully extended to 2 m (6 ft). Lines from the main hydraulic power unit run to the jaw. The jaw is equipped with quick disconnects which mate with similar connections on the hydraulic tools. This permits hydraulic power to be coupled underwater and transmitted to the tool when it is grasped without the need for hoses on each tool.

The tools are held by compliant brushes in a tubular aluminum holder which is positioned opposite the primary manipulator and normally out of the frontal viewing area. The holder can be extended so that the tools are extracted or replaced along a radial line corresponding to the manipulator's linear extension capability, thus shortening the time required to perform a tool exchange. Bits, such as drills or sockets, are held in clips along the upper and outside edge of the holder.

It was envisioned that the WSP would do the work of divers operating at great depths; therefore, large tools are not included. The tools provided are the type and size that would normally be used by a mechanic performing field operations on land. The tool suite was selected on the basis of work functions required to perform typical underwater tasks, such as those encountered in salvage operations. These include debris clearance, hull penetration, lift device attachment, and salvage valve coupling attachment. The tools are divided into three categories: rotary, linear, and power velocity (explosively actuated). Hydraulic operation was selected for most tools, as well as for the manipulators and other actuators, because of its inherent advantages of precise control, high power density, and insensitivity to depth pressure. The rotary tools, which include a high- and low-speed drill, a reciprocating knife, an impact wrench, a winch, and a chipping hammer, are powered by small, fixed-displacement piston motors. The linear tools, which include a jack, a spreader, and a cable cutter, are operated by linear actuators. Both types represent a pioneering effort toward a comprehensive underwater tool suite. The power-velocity tools, cable cutter, and stud driver are used in applications where a high-energy output for a short duration is desired. They are simple and easy to operate but can be used only once during an operation. Consequently, several spaces in the tool holder are reserved for these tools.

The tools of an oceanographer are often required aboard undersea vehicles for scientific investigations. Marine corers and grabbers have been adapted to specific vehicle manipulators, so that the oceanographic investigator can carefully select the location on the sea floor from which he or she wishes a sample. Water samplers, with many barrels, are utilized with remotely selected filling capability. Photography, both movie and still, continues to be a major tool of the undersea geologist and biologist. With the increased interests in offshore resource exploitation, sea floor surveys for manganese nodules and for other geologic characteristics are requiring the adaptation of increasing numbers of scientists' tools and measuring devices to operations from undersea work vehicles.

Power Supplies

Vehicles and other components of undersea work systems that must traverse through the sea and perform functions within the sea are critically dependent on their power supplies. For cable-controlled systems, electrical power is provided by the cable with trade-offs required in regard to voltage, frequency, and data bandwidth versus cable size, weight, length, etc. But for free-swimming manned or unmanned systems, self-contained power supplies are required. Batteries and fuel cells are the primary candidates for providing power sources for noncabled systems.

Archeologists have found batteries made by the Parthians who lived in the Baghdad region between 250 B.C. and 224 A.D. The copper-iron combination in these ancient batteries is the same as that which Luigi Galvani used in 1786 when he "discovered" the galvanic cell. Batteries of the carbon-zinc dry cells and rechargeable lead-sulfuric acid cells have become the workhorses of current applications, with alkaline and mercury dry cells and nickel-cadmium rechargeable batteries also in common use. For high-power, short-term output, rechargeable silver-zinc batteries have been developed for applications such as torpedo operations. Lead-acid "golf-cart"-type rechargeable batteries have become extremely reliable, are low cost, and have a reasonable power density of about 20 W hr/lb or about 50 W hr/kg. Since these batteries can be operated in a pressure-compensated environment, and thereby not require heavy pressure-resistant cases, they are particularly attractive for undersea applications.

With the energy crisis becoming felt throughout the world, particularly due to the uncertainties in petroleum supplies, considerable development effort is being applied to alternate power sources. An important part of this effort is directed toward the development of dependable, safe, high-energy-density electric batteries for application to automobiles and other petroleum-dependent devices. Included are batteries based on the following materials: nickel-cadmium, silver-cadmium, magnesium-seawater, zinc-air, iron-air, iron-nickel, silver-iron, mercury oxide-zinc, magnesium dioxide-alkaline zinc, lithium organic, and lithium inorganic. These developments should be closely monitored, because batteries of higher power capacity will most surely result.

As an example of current research and development that may result in a major leap forward in battery capabilities, let us look at the lithium inorganic type. Lithium cells have a potential for about 40 times the energy density of lead acid cells. A number of companies are currently developing the lithium inorganic electrolyte battery, in various sizes, for government and industrial uses. This development effort has emphasized the thionyl chloride reaction, since it produces the most energy density of the sealed cells. Cells can be configured for low rates of 1 month (550 W hr/kg and 0.92 W hr/cm^3) to very high rates of 10 min (220 W hr/kg and 0.37 W hr/cm^3). This is by far superior performance when compared with other battery and engine systems for marine propulsion applications. The cell sizes manufactured range from 1 to 15,000 A hr. Test programs have aided in the identification of many deficiencies with the present large-size, high-rate cells. Many of the deficiencies can be readily corrected, but others are less understood, and additional development is continuing. Cells up to the 500-A-hr size have been designed for spacecraft use. It is believed that this cell technology will produce an excellent high-energy-density, underwater power source.

Fuel cells have been used extensively in space applications. Conversion efficiencies as high as 80% can be achieved by various combinations of fuels, oxidants, and catalysts. The Pratt Whitney Company has developed cells that have been tested for undersea applications in a Perry submersible. For like electric characteristics, a typical fuel cell is about one-half the weight and one-half the volume of a similar silver-zinc battery.

Propulsion

All undersea work vehicles use propellers to provide thrust for maneuverability. Some high-speed devices, such as torpedoes, make use of solid or liquid propellents and obtain thrust by rocket-type action, but for our discussion on undersea work systems, slower and highly maneuverable systems are required. These systems have propellers that are primarily in open water, driving the vehicle forward like a ship's propeller, but they may also have propellers that are shrouded to provide a nozzle effect or ducted to provide a pumping-type water jet effect.

The simplest and most often used thruster is a propeller attached to an electric motor. The amount of thrust then varies with the size and shape of the propeller and speed of the motor. Most free-swimming vehicles with battery power supplies use dc motors with continuous speed control. Cable-controlled vehicles can take advantage of their higher power capacity and usually use high-voltage ac motors. Each of the motors is usually oil-filled and pressure-compensated to keep seawater leakage problems to a minimum and to alleviate the problems with high-pressure rotary mechanical seals.

For certain applications, particularly for cabled systems at deep depths, hydraulic motors are used to drive the propellers. For this type of system, a single electric motor drives a hydraulic pump that keeps a reservoir of fluid at a set differential pressure above the ambient sea pressure. Then, by remotely controlled *servo valves,* the pressurized fluid is routed, at various rates, to the propeller motors of choice. Hydraulic propulsion systems have the following advantages: They have a continuous electrical load requirement, thereby eliminating surges in the cable each time a motor speed is adjusted; hydraulic motors are smaller and lighter in weight than electric motors; a slight outward leak of hydraulic oil is not as damaging as a slight inward leak of seawater into an electric motor; and the total horsepower available on a vehicle can be applied to any thruster rather than having each thruster limited by its motor's electrical characteristics.

Shrouding a propeller has two effects. First, a proper hydrodynamically designed shroud will increase the effective thrust for the propeller for low-velocity conditions, giving it a *Kort nozzle* effect. When space and weight allow, this increase in thrust can be most advantageous. The second effect is the protection of the propeller from being bumped against obstructions or entangling in debris. Special care must be taken in the placement of thrusters on a vehicle to provide locations with unobstructed water flow to optimize thrust but to minimize the possibility of damage or entanglement of the propellers. These two diametrically opposed requirements are the subject of some of the most complex trade-off during vehicle design. In fact, several vehicles have totally enclosed propellers that look more like pumps, with a pump jet-type thrust, accepted for safety even at a loss of efficiency of energy conversion.

Bibliography

Booda, L. L. (1976). Glass microspheres essential ingredient of flotation foam, Sea Technology, Vol. 17, No. 4, April 1976.

Booda, L. L. (1978). Loran C. Omega navigation systems near completion, Sea Technology, Vol. 19, No. 3, March 1978.

Bridges, R. M. (1977). Undersea cables for instrumentation, Sea Technology, Vol. 18, No. 5, May 1977.

Busby, R. F. (1978). Underwater Inspection, Testing, Monitoring of Offshore Structures. NOAA Office of Ocean Engineering, Rockville, Md.

Cohen, T. J. (1976). Microprocessor technology—an electronic revolution, Sea Technology, Vol. 17, No. 3, March 1976.

Cowen, S. J. (1979). Fiber optic video transmission system employing pulse frequency modulation, Proceedings Oceans '79. Institute of Electrical and Electronic Engineers, San Diego.

Cowen, S., Wilkins, G., and Eastley, R. A. (1978). Recent Progress in Optical Fiber Cables for Use in the Ocean. National Telecommunications Conference, Los Angeles.

Estabrook, N., Wheeler, H., Uhler, D., and Hackman, D. (1975). Development of a deep ocean work system, Proceedings Oceans '75. Institute of Electrical and Electronic Engineers, San Diego.

Heckman, P., and McCardell, P. (1978). Real time optical mapping system, Proceedings SPIE 1978 Conference, Vol. 160. Society of Photographic Instrumentation Engineers.

Hood, H. A. (1975). Aramid (KEVLAR) use in parallel yarn ropes, Sea Technology, Vol. 16, No. 7, July 1975.

LaQue, F.L. (1978). OTEC component materials typical for survival in the sea, Sea Technology, Vol. 19, No. 2, February 1978.

Lund, T. J. (1979). Application of lithium-thionyl chloride batteries to marine requirements, in Proceedings Oceans '79. Institute of Electrical and Electronic Engineers, San Diego.

McCartney, J. F. (1979). Development of a high energy density battery for undersea applications, in Proceedings Oceans '79. Institute of Electrical and Electronic Engineers, San Diego.

Nagy, A. (1977). Navigation and positioning systems come of age, Sea Technology, Vol. 18, No. 3, March 1977.

Porta, D. W. (1977). An acoustic navigation system for offshore positioning applications, Sea Technology, Vol. 18, No. 5, May 1977.

Riewald, P. G. (1979). Performance bases for the use of aramid fiber in marine applications, in *Proceedings Oceans '79*. Institute of Electrical and Electronic Engineers, San Diego.

Ross, R. W. (1978). Corrosion of steel in the marine environment, *Sea Technology*, Vol. 19, No. 2, February 1978.

Stachiw, J. D. (1977). Nonmetallic materials for offshore engineering, in *Proceedings Second Ship Technology and Research Symposium*, paper T8-2. Society of Naval Architects and Marine Engineers, San Francisco.

Stachiw, J. D. (1977). Spherical sector windows with restrained edge for undersea applications, *Journal of Engineering for Industry, Transactions*, Vol. 99, Series B, No. 2.

Sutton, J. L. (1977). State of the art in underwater acoustic imaging, in *Proceedings of Ocean '77 Symposium*. Ocean '77 Symposium, Los Angeles.

Sutton, J. L. (1978). Description of a navy holographic underwater acoustic imaging system, in *Proceedings of Acoustic Imaging Symposium*. Acoustic Imaging Symposium, Key West, Fla.

Sutton, J. L. (1979). Pressure tolerant electronics, in *Proceedings Oceans '79*. Institute of Electrical and Electronic Engineers, San Diego.

Talkington, H. R. (1978). Underwater work systems research and development, in *Proceedings Offshore Technology Conference 1978*. Houston.

Wernli, R. L. (1978). Design for Remote Work in the Deep Ocean, ASME 78-WA/OCE-4. American Society of Mechanical Engineers, New York.

Wernli, R. L. (1979). The work systems package—remote work experience, in *Proceedings Oceans '79*. Institute of Electrical and Electronic Engineers, San Diego.

6
Design, Construction, and Testing

The basis of undersea work systems is the submersible vehicle that transports the sensors and supports the tools and sampling devices at the work scene. The shape and internal configuration of manned vehicles are controlled by their primary element, the large pressure hull that houses the operators. Most manned vehicles are assembled around spheres, multispheres, or cylinders, with the remainder of the equipment packaged on a framework assembled closely about the pressure hull. Unmanned remotely controlled vehicles, as shown in Figure 6-1, usually have a rectangular boxlike framework onto which the various items of equipment are attached. The relative locations and interrelationship of these equipment items are very important to a successfully operating system. This chapter contains a series of descriptions and observations of design parameters based on past experience in development and operation of many types of undersea work systems. These items may be applied as guidelines to assist the neophyte designer in selecting methods of approach to the design of systems and their individual components.

Arrangement

Initially, vehicle dynamics must be carefully considered when defining the arrangement of equipment aboard an undersea vehicle. The need to balance

61

Figure 6-1   Open frame construction of CURV II. (U.S. Navy.)

the center of thrust for the horizontal (both forward-aft and transverse) and the vertical thrusters with the static centerlines of buoyancy, gravity, and tether drag (if any) is critical to the design. In addition, the following need to be considered. The structural frame should be as lightweight as possible since its weight, like all weight on a submersible vehicle, must ultimately be compensated by some buoyancy material to render the total system slightly positively buoyant. But the frame must also be structurally adequate to support all the components and sufficiently rugged to absorb impacts due to handling and inadvertent bottoming. The strength-to-weight trade-off for the basic structural frame requires very careful analysis and clever attention to detail.

Whether to install a fairing around the vehicle to give a streamlining effect must be decided not on the basis of appearance but on the potential missions. For high-speed requirements, where skin drag is an important characteristic, a fairing should certainly be considered. The additional weight of a fairing may well be overshadowed by the increase to the speed-power ratio. However, if the primary application of the vehicle requires slow, precise maneuverability to accomplish work at a sea floor site, then a fairing acts as a large sail area with respect to undersea currents; thus an open framework is more desirable.

When determining the location of the thrusters, both the potential for entanglement and stirring of the sea floor sediments must be considered. The dichotomy of wanting open undisturbed water at both ends of each thruster and the wish to protect the thrusters from ingesting foreign matter must be carefully observed and clever trade-offs effected. Usually the thrusters are placed high on the vehicle's frame, so that the suction and thrusted volumes are as far from the sea floor as possible. Most of the dangers of entanglement are near the sea floor, so that placing the thrusters high on the frame also minimizes these problems. The other primary danger of entanglement is due to standing cables and lines that may be buoyed or guyed to structures. To minimize this hazard, the thrusters should be inboard of the framework and suitable guards installed to deflect any external cables or lines.

Obviously, the navigation and monitoring sensors must be mounted on the forward part of the frame overlooking the location of the tool suite to provide the operator with proper observation for conducting operations. This need to colocate much of the weight-producing and volume-using devices causes a trim problem in regard to vehicle buoyancy as well as a problem in allocation of the critically small amounts of space on the front end of vehicles. Usually, thrusters and auxiliary equipment that are not location-dependent may be placed in the afterpart of the frame to balance the mass of the sensors and tools up forward and, along with some movable ballast, provide for adequate trim and roll stability. The allocation of forward-looking space is most critical, and careful analysis must be made of range of operations of the tools, the field of view of the sensors (both acoustic and optical), and the illumination field of the lights (see example in Fig. 6-2). Sometimes clever applications of folding or retracting systems are required to sequentially place devices in common locations dependent on the time of their need during mission operations.

As noted, it is desirable to maintain the final vehicle system in a mode of positive buoyancy. This is primarily a safety requirement to allow surfacing if thruster power fails and to provide ease of recovery of the vehicle from the sea surface after completion of each dive. Usually ballast or noncritical components are arranged to be released to provide even more buoyancy for ascent in case of emergency. To provide for normal operating buoyancy, all the underwater weight of the vehicle system must be compensated for by addition of fixed buoyancy. For shallow operations this may be accomplished by high volume-to-weight ratio cylinders, but for deeper operations syntactic foam is most commonly used. A section in Chapter 5 includes data on syntactic foam and other buoyancy materials. Since buoyancy requires volume and weight, every effort should be taken to keep the underwater weight as well as space required for each component of the

Figure 6-2   Front view of CURV III showing locations of sensors, lights, and tools. (U.S. Navy.)

vehicle system to a minimum. A slight increase in weight of a component is compounded by buoyancy requirement and directly affects the mass of the system, with serious implications to thrust and maneuverability characteristics and surface handling requirements.

To provide a vehicle that has a strong righting moment and is a stable platform on which to mount sensors and tools, an acceptable center of buoyancy (CB) to center of gravity (CG) separation must be achieved. To accomplish this, the buoyancy material is always placed as high as possible and the heaviest items placed as low as possible as in the vehicle shown in Figure 6-3. The resultant upward vertical force due to buoyancy and the downward vertical force due to gravity provide a righting couple, when an external perturbing force tends to tip the vehicle from its stable condition.

Two items regarding safety must be considered during this phase of design. The optical imaging system, usually television cameras, should be placed in such locations and provided with adequate motion to observe the sides and top of the vehicle as well as the work area to allow for diagnosing entanglement or jamming problems. All tools that might become entangled in the course of their operation must be designed with an emergency jettison

Figure 6-3 Simple configuration of hydraulic SNOOPY. (U.S. Navy.)

feature. A general safety review should be required during design, to include all parts of the vehicle system, to minimize the potential of entanglement with objects near the sea floor or other events that might prevent returning to the surface.

Interrelation of Equipment

The interrelation or relative location of equipment mounted on a submersible vehicle must be given constant attention during design and construction. As noted, the concurrent requirements of the sensors, their illuminators, and working tools are very important in determining arrangement. In addition to their joint support, such items as electrical and acoustic interference must be considered. A flashing strobe light for still photography may optically blind a nearby television camera for some period of time or may electrically interfere with a high-resolution sonar image if not properly designed as part of the total system.

A particularly difficult problem to overcome, if not considered and resolved in the initial design, is the acoustic and electrical noise created by surging loads on the electric or hydraulic motors that drive the thrusters and the electrohydraulic pump units. These items are large power consumers and, due to the nature of their operation, are continually changing in the amount of electrical energy being transmitted. If not considered very carefully, these surges in the system cabling, especially the vehicle tether (if there is one), can have very serious effects on the instrumentation circuits, which by their very nature are operating at very low power levels and are susceptible to interference by large power changes. In addition, the acoustic noise inherent in hydraulic pumps can interfere with acoustic sensors unless location is carefully considered and baffling provided. Some relief from this problem is possible by carefully selecting the materials and clearances within the pump and carefully maintaining them. Some advantages can be accrued by measuring the spectral output of the pump's noise and operating the acoustic sensors only in frequency regimes of lowest interference.

Tethered systems have a particularly bothersome problem of electromagnetic interference (EMI) due to the tether itself. The portion of the tether that is exposed to the air, that is, the part on a storage drum on board the support ship or in the air between the storage drum and the sea surface, makes a marvelous antenna. Radio, radar, and any other radiation may be picked up by this "antenna" portion of the tether and provide disabling interference to low-level instrumentation signals. Good solid metallic shielding can protect the circuits from this source of EMI, but "good solid metallic" shielding is heavy. Vehicle tethers are very weight-conscious, particularly the portion of the cable near the vehicle, which is often made buoyant. Special design effort is required to defeat the EMI problem while keeping the cable lightweight. This is a natural application for fiber optic data leads, as discussed in Chapter 5.

Ease of maintenance and troubleshooting must be considered in the location of equipment within a vehicle system. To the maximum extent possible, modular design for ease of replacement of defective parts and automatic fault location circuitry should be applied. Accessibility of components including ease of disassembly of pressure cases and disconnection of electrical connectors involves special problems to be considered during the design of undersea systems. And, always, great care must be taken to provide good electrical grounding consistently throughout the system.

Testing

A properly planned and executed test program is vital to a successful development program. This is particularly true for undersea systems, due to the rigorous environmental conditions encountered during operations. Often such constraints as cost and schedule apply pressures to shorten or curtail adequate testing. If a reliable and capable system is desired, adequate testing must be accomplished.

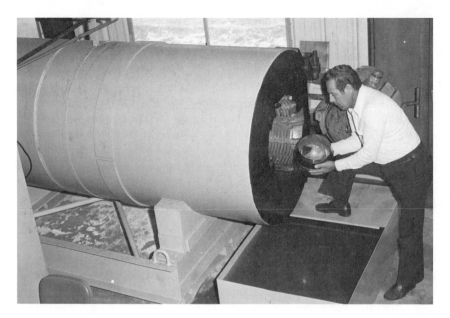

Figure 6-4   Preparation for a test in high-pressure test facility. (U.S. Navy.)

Testing should begin in the component phase, with both laboratory demonstration of operation and pressure tank tests required (Fig. 6-4). As much as possible, the individual components should be tested in simulated operation during pressure tests, not just static "squeeze" tests. During assembly of components, major subsystems should be given time to "burn in" on the laboratory benches to eliminate defective parts prior to "going to sea."

Dip tests in shallow water are required for the assembled system: first to ascertain weight, buoyancy, trim, CB and CG, and such static in-water characteristics and second to test the operation of subsystems in a wet environment. The first dip test may well be quite extensive as a time for troubleshooting and optimizing subsystems.

After all components have been pressure-tested and the assembled system has been dip-tested, a full-scale pressure test of the operating system should be conducted if adequate facilities are available. Problems can be found, diagnosed, and resolved much easier and at lower cost in the controlled conditions of a simulated ocean pressure test facility than during a sea operation. A proper pressure test program will start with an intermediate depth requirement and progressively increase pressure until the maximum safety factor is proven, then cycle to that pressure several times (a minimum

68

of seven), and then hold the system under pressure for periods of time corresponding to mission dive requirements.

After adequate laboratory and pressure tests, a carefully planned initial sea operation may be conducted as part of the test program. Each step should be scheduled to prove certain components prior to risking the full system. Then a series of full-system tests may be scheduled to prove system capability, safety, and reliability. For manned systems, there are special criteria, established by certifying agencies, that must be met prior to allowing manned occupancy during operations. These certification requirements are well defined, and requirement documents are available.

Documentation

To support safe, efficient, and reliable operations, a complete and carefully validated set of documents is required. "Validated" includes not only carefully written documents but also detailed checks of the documents by dry runs accomplished with the actual equipment, including insertion of simulated failures to test emergency modes of control.

The documentation package includes a complete set of construction drawings that must be continually updated with proper configuration control techniques, operating manuals for each portion of the system, maintenance manuals, emergency procedures, and spare parts lists. The Marine Technology Society (MTS) has published two very good manuals on submerged vehicle design and safety and a third manual on safety systems, procedures, and personnel selection and training. These three documents are the collection of knowledge of a large number of designers, operators, and certifying agencies, and they provide excellent guidance to developers of undersea systems.

Bibliography

Brahtz, J. F. (1968). *Ocean Engineering, System Planning and Design*. Wiley, New York.

Goodfellow, R. (1977). *Underwater Engineering*. Petroleum Publishing Co., Tulsa.

Myers, J. D. (1969). *Handbook of Ocean and Underwater Engineering*. McGraw-Hill, New York.

Piccard, A. (1956). *Earth, Sky and Sea*. Oxford University Press, New York.

Talkington, H. R. (1978). Underwater work systems research and development, in *Proceedings Offshore Technology Conference 1978*. Houston.

Undersea Vehicle Committee (1968). Safety and Operational Guidelines for Undersea Vehicles, Book I. Marine Technology Society, Washington, D.C.

Undersea Vehicle Committee (1974). Safety and Operational Guidelines for Undersea Vehicles, Book II. Marine Technology Society, Washington, D.C.

Undersea Vehicle Committee (1979). International Safety Standard Guidelines for the Operation of Undersea Vehicles. Marine Technology Society, Washington, D.C.

7
Support Services

A vital portion of every operation concerning undersea work systems is the support required to prepare, transport, handle, and communicate with the working vehicle. The surface support craft, with its handling system and shipboard equipment, must be capable of transporting the work system and its crew to the worksite and then providing the tending requirements during the submerged portion of the operations. A large percentage of the failures of operations may be directly ascribed to lack of adequate planning or suitable capability of the surface support systems.

Surface Support Craft

The surface support craft designated to participate in operations involving undersea work systems must be so selected and outfitted that it, in a support capacity, is not the weak link in the chain of operability. The size and tending requirements of the work system, the location and sea conditions of the worksite, and the control and communications requirements for the operation must all be considered in the selection of a suitable craft. Often the overriding requirement is the stability of the support craft. The response of the craft when subjected to the pitch, heave, and roll induced by the expected sea state determines the effects of the dynamic loadings on the handling (e.g., launch and recovery) of the undersea vehicle. For this reason, a variety of sizes and configurations of ships is utilized for this purpose, each carefully matched to the system it supports.

For operations under difficult weather conditions, like in the North Sea, fairly large ships are required. Good examples for this type of operation are the ships operated by Vickers in support to their manned PISCES-type submersibles. These ships have been specially modified with stern ramps and overhead beams to launch and retrieve submersibles in sea states up to five. They have space aboard to store, repair, and service two submersibles at one time. The handling is accomplished by running the ship slowly into the wind, thereby creating a small area of relative calm on the sea surface directly behind the ship, and launching and retrieving through this area. Keeping the ship under way and operating from the stern also minimizes the dynamic motions (particularly roll and heave) due to the sea action on the ship. Operating ships of this size are quite costly and can only be justified by a high use factor.

Smaller ships are used in areas where the operations are not as sea state limited and for handling smaller-sized undersea systems. The smaller craft are less costly and may be leased for short periods of time for operations that do not require continuous long-term capability. The matching of the handling system and technique to the vehicle mass, and to the ship's dynamic characteristics, is much more important when operating with small craft than with large. There is just not as great a safety factor, and careful planning and crew training are essential.

An additional means to provide safe control of undersea systems during handling through the air-sea interface is to work through the center of motion of the support ship, that is, through a center well. Catamaran-type hulls are especially adaptable to this technique. The LULU handles the DSV ALVIN in this manner as do the two U.S. Navy ASR's (submarine rescue ships) USS Pigeon and USS Ortalan for support to the MK II deep diving systems. The center well provides an area of relative calm sea surface and minimum of ship's heave, pitch, and roll. If the configuration of the support craft allows, this is one of the best means to handle undersea systems.

The offshore oil industry has found that the best way to conduct operations through the sea surface with minimum downtime due to weather is to use semisubmersible platforms. The semi-submersible concept has been applied to mobile craft as well and has proven to provide a stable work surface for a variety of sea operations, including handling of undersea work systems. An important development in this type of craft is the SWATH (small waterplane area twin hulled) ship. The SWATH ship's capabilities are achieved by placing the greater poriton of the ship's buoyant volume below the sea surface and supporting the above-surface structure by thin struts which are little affected by wave action. Stability is exceptional both under way and at rest in sea states up to seven. The concept includes full automatic control over pitch, heave, roll, yaw, and sway.

Figure 7-1   Stable semisubmersible platform SSP KAIMALINO. (U.S. Navy.)

An example of a SWATH ship is the 190-ton stable semisubmerged platform (SSP KAIMALINO), shown in Figure 7-1, which was designed and developed to satisfy a need for a small, oceangoing work platform which would have the reduced motion, greater deck space, and higher speed of much larger conventional monohulls. The SSP measures 27 m (89 ft) in length and 14 m (45 ft) in width. The vessel was designed by personnel at the Naval Ocean Systems Center Hawaii Laboratory with support from the Pearl Harbor Naval Shipyard; it was constructed at the Coast Guard Yard at Curtis Bay, Maryland. The SSP has two submerged, parallel, torpedolike hulls which support a cross structure above water by means of four stream-lined, vertical, surface-piercing struts. Two controllable canard fins are located near the hull bows, and a full-span stabilizing fin with controllable flaps is near the hull stern. The fins provide dynamic stability, damping, and control over heave, pitch, and roll. The design configuration of the SSP will permit normal operations in 3-m (9-ft) waves. With a full fuel complement of 18.8 tons, the SSP will have an operating range of approximately 350 nautical miles at a cruise speed of 12 m/sec (24 knots). Two T64-GE-6B turboshaft engines of approximately 2000 hp each are used to drive 2-m-diameter (78 in.), controllable and reversible pitch propellers.

An innovative technique for supporting submersible operations was developed in the Hawaii area where the sea surface is always rough and the majority of dive sites is near to land-based servicing facilities. This technique, initially developed by personnel at the Makai Range and later improved at the Naval Oceans Systems Center (NOSC) Hawaii Laboratory, is based on the use of a submergible barge which, when controlled by divers, can dive in a horizontal attitude to a predetermined depth, hover, and then return to the surface. The submergible barge is basically two horizontal cylindrical pontoons with a supporting cross structure. The pontoons include both fixed-buoyancy chambers and variable-buoyancy (floodable) chambers. Compressed air in high-pressure cylinders is carried on deck to blow the water ballast out for vertical control. The operating scenario for both the Makai LRT (launch retrieval transport) and the NOSC LARP (launch and recovery platform), shown in Figure 7-2, is as follows: The submersible system (manned or unmanned) is serviced and prepared at a shore site. The vehicle is then placed on the LARP and towed, on the surface, to the dive site. Divers board the LARP and by operating flooding valves dive the LARP to a depth below the sea's surface action [usually 15–23 m (50–75 ft)]. The submersible is then released and swims away to perform its mission. The LARP may be left at depth or brought back to the surface to await the submersible's return. Upon return, the submersible docks on the

Figure 7-2   Submergible launch and recovery platform (LARP). (U.S. Navy.)

LARP, at depth. Then the LARP surfaces and is taken under tow back to the dock at the shore service area. Alternate means of operations include controlling the diving and surfacing of the LARP remotely by cable from the towing craft and controlling the depth of operation of the LARP by tethering a buoy on a preset length of line. This technique provides a very cost-effective means to operate undersea vehicles when repeated operations are near a servicing site.

Shipboard Handling Systems

Ships of medium and small size can be utilized in temperate climates where the sea conditions do not cause high dynamic loads. Often a hydraulically operated A-frame pivoting over the stern of the craft provides a suitable handling capability. Some craft have been outfitted with modified land-based cranes fixed to the deck. Standard cranes with a high boom have been used successfully in low sea states, but the pendulum effect due to the high "pick point" can cause dangerous conditions if the sea state increases. A more preferred technique is to provide a means to control the lateral motion of the vehicle during its handling. This has been accomplished by installing an articulated crane with a boom that reaches right down to the sea surface. While several crane types have been specially constructed for this purpose, short-term operations have been successfully conducted using a modified "back hoe" digging crane like the one shown in Figure 7-3. When operating with these cranes, provision is usually made to provide high-speed line pull, so that the submersible may be picked off of the top of a swell by careful timing of the crane's lifting line coordinated with precise maneuvering of the support craft. Pivoting A-frame-shaped booms, such as shown in Figure 7-4, are used successfully on a number of craft.

Cranes with stabilized booms, such as shown in Figures 7-5 and 7-6, have been developed to handle loads at sea. These handling systems are characterized by mechanically stabilizing the lifting boom, thereby effectively holding the boom steady relative to a point in space and decoupled from the ship's motions. This may be accomplished either with a passive system of masses and dashpots or actively with motion sensors, synchros, and motors. Passive systems, as the name implies, are systems that mechanically react to forces applied to them by such means as springs and counterweights. Active systems require sensors to detect forces and power systems to drive the boom or block in some direction to minimize action of the impinging force. Passive systems, while usually large and bulky, suffice to protect the loads being handled in medium sea states, but active systems are often required to safely protect large loads in high seas. Either way, the objective is to remove the ship's motion from the dynamic process of lifting

Figure 7-3 Back-hoe-type crane with the Westinghouse DEEPSTAR. (U.S. Navy.)

Figure 7-4 Pivoting A-frame handling system for the Straza SCARAB. (Ametek Straza.)

Figure 7-5 Stabilized boom handling system for RUWS. (U.S. Navy.)

Figure 7-6 Rapid pickup handling system for the Harbor Branch JOHNSON-SEALINK. (Harbor Branch Foundation, Inc.)

the submersible from the sea. This type of system is especially applicable for handling cable-controlled unmanned systems, since the cable continues to need tending throughout the diving mission. For safest operations in areas where sea conditions can rapidly change, a capability to provide launch and recovery of undersea vehicles with full control of lateral motions is strongly recommended.

Shipboard Equipment

The support equipment aboard the surface craft must be carefully planned, designed, and installed as an integrated part of the total work system. Most often the ship assignments may change; therefore the support suite must be capable of rapid removal and reinstallation. The following are a set of notes on items to consider in preparing shipboard equipment.

A modular approach for all components of shipboard equipment is recommended. The control and monitoring station can best be installed and checked out in a van-type enclosure and then placed aboard ship in a complete and ready condition. Each other item should be wired and checked out, with connectors (both electrical and mechanical) on pretested cables ready for rapid installation. An example of this type of modular system is shown in Figure 7-7.

For cable-controlled systems, the handling and stowage of the cable are especially important. The winches and slip rings require careful attention during installation and maintenance. The cable itself must be protected from abrasion, electromagnetic interference (EMI), and overheating due to internal power transmission. As noted in Chapter 5, primary goals in the design of tether cables are a small cross-sectional area and light weight. To achieve these, the electrical shielding is kept to a minimum. Shielding that is adequate within the cable may not be adequate to shield the EMI from the signal leads for the portion of the cable that is out of the water, including that part wrapped on the winch drum. Some winch designs must include EMI shielding of the stowage drum and air or water for cooling.

The support ship must have good maneuvering control. Precise ship positioning is required to launch and retrieve manned submersibles and to hold position over the worksite for tethered vehicles. As a minimum, the support craft should be one with twin propulsors to allow careful differential control with the two propellers. The addition of a bow thruster greatly assists in station keeping. The ultimate is a ship with cycloidal propellers or similar thrusters that provide equal maneuverability in all directions. For short-term emergency operations, adequate station keeping has been accomplished by

Figure 7-7   Modular handling and stowage system for Hydro Products' RCVs. (Hydro Products, Inc.)

tying two craft bow to bow and using one propulsor against the other. This method is tedious and recommended only as a last resort. Station keeping on a particular geographic position can be achieved only if a navigation system adequate for the precision required is available. The existing surface navigation systems in the worksite area must initially be assessed and a special system provided if normal coverage cannot provide the inputs necessary to successfully accomplish the task.

Adequate space must be designated for spare parts storage and to accomplish repair and maintenance on the undersea systems. The equipment to support these tasks should be in a small van or other easily transportable container that also provides easy accessibility while onboard the ship. In addition, a minimum amount of equipment should be available to assist in recovering the undersea system should it become disabled on the sea floor or the sea surface. Recommended rescue or "self-help" devices and equipment are listed and defined in Chapter 9.

Intership communications are vital for a safe and successful operation. These include communication among the undersea system control point, the ship's bridge, the launch and retrieval location, the cable winch (if there is one), and the regular radio communication center. In addition, for manned submersible operations, underwater acoustic communications are a must. Radio communications must be provided to other ships involved in the operation, to home base, and to other craft that might inadvertently enter the operating area and thereby become a hazard to the undersea system.

Transportation

The transportation of undersea work systems and their support equipment is usually accomplished by shipping them aboard the craft that will later support them during their operations at sea. As noted, a modular approach is recommended for rapid installation and removal. The same modular approach greatly assists in transshipping the equipment from one site to another. The "containerized"-type modules should include the requirements for "forklift" positions and special slings for lifting.

Certain types of undersea systems may be called upon to participate in emergency situations. For these systems, aircraft loading plans should be prepared as part of the original documentation—including weight distribution, size, shape, and arrangement for several classes of aircraft. It is also helpful to prepare the containerized module to conform to the automatic loading pallet specifications for cargo aircraft or to easily fit upon the automatic loading pallets. In designing for shock and vibration, it should be noted that the most rigorous environment will most likely be that encountered during transportation. Very good specifications are available that define the shock and vibration environment that can be expected in the various transportation media. These specifications should be judiciously applied in the planning and design of all systems.

Base Support

Undersea work systems require more than just buildings and piers at their land support base. Certainly, adequate shop space is necessary for repair, maintenance, and improvements to the system and the storage of spare parts. But, due to the potential risk to human life, adequate space and aids for training as well as continued update of certified documentation is required. Reliable communications from the support base to the operating craft, to the support bases of other operators, and to cognizant emergency agencies are important. Preplanned, well-documented, and well-exercised emergency plans must be available, along with the required equipment. Organizations that operate undersea vehicles, whether manned or unmanned, must always be ready to respond to the emergency call for help from a group with a distressed system. The discussion on operations, in Chapter 9, includes some recommendations for self-help equipment and procedures as well as advice on how to help and to receive help from others.

Bibliography

Booda, L. L. (1976). Deck gear on the job for research and industry, *Sea Technology*, Vol. 17, No. 8, July 1976.

Busby, R. F. (1978). Underwater Inspection, Testing, Monitoring of Offshore Structures. NOAA Office of Ocean Engineering, Rockville, Md.

Crenshaw, R. S. (1960). Naval Shiphandling. U.S. Naval Institute, Annapolis, Md.

Goodfellow, R. (1977). *Underwater Engineering*. Petroleum Publishing Co., Tulsa.

Lloyd's Register of Shipping (1978). Register of Offshore Units, Submersibles and Diving Systems, 1977–78. Lloyd's Register of Shipping, London.

Mulcahy, M. (1976). U.S. Navy's KAIMALINO—a stable semisubmersible platform, *Sea Technology*, Vol. 17, No. 8, August 1976.

Mulcahy, M. (1979). Scientists articulate deck equipment needs for research vessels, *Sea Technology*, Vol. 20, No. 7, July 1979.

Ploegert, J. C. (1975). How to pick special purpose shipboard winches, *Sea Technology*, Vol. 16, No. 7, July 1975.

8
Existing Systems

To perform undersea tasks, total systems must include transporters to provide mobility and motive power for the working tools and support to the sensors needed for acquisition and monitoring of the worksite. These transporters may range from a human diver, for minor shallow-water work, through a range of tethered and untethered, manned and unmanned submersible systems. Both diver and manned systems are well covered elsewhere; therefore, in this chapter we shall concentrate on the application of remotely controlled unmanned systems, with descriptions of selected types of diving and manned submersible systems.

Unmanned Tethered Vehicles

Although these tethered vehicle systems are referred to as unmanned, this does not mean that people have been removed from the system; it simply implies that the human operator is not aboard the vehicle at the worksite. The human operator is totally integrated into the system and has full perception because of displays from the sensors aboard the vehicle and the controls for its operation. Thus, these vehicles would be more properly termed "remotely manned undersea vehicles."

U.S. Government Systems. At the Naval Oceans Systems Center (NOSC), San Diego, California, a broad family of undersea submersible systems has been developed since the first experimental undersea recovery systems in 1956. The following are examples of tethered unmanned vehicles of various sizes and capabilities to match varying requirements.

Cable-Controlled Underwater Recovery Vehicle: CURV I. The first remotely controlled maneuverable tethered unmanned undersea vehicle developed at the NOSC was the CURV I (cable-controlled underwater recovery vehicle). It was developed in the late 1950s to perform recovery tasks for torpedo and undersea missile programs. It was retired in 1967, and many of its components and sensors were incorporated into the more advanced and deeper-operating CURV II. During the operating life of the CURV I, it performed hundreds of missions including the recovery of more than 100 torpedoes from the sea floor. A high point in its brief career was its participation in the search for the hydrogen bomb in the ocean's depths off Palomares, Spain in 1966. It was the CURV I that made the actual attachments to the bomb that enabled the final recovery and thereby the termination of that 81-day operation.

Cable-Controlled Underwater Recovery Vehicle: CURV II. CURV II is an unmanned tethered submersible capable of operating to 760 m (2500 ft). It is the successor to CURV I. The configuration of CURV II, shown in Figure 4-7, is typical of most unmanned vehicles; it has an open rectangular framework to support the sensors and tools, two horizontal propulsion motors to drive and steer the vehicle, one vertical motor for close vertical control, and a net positive buoyancy of approximately 11 kg (25 lb). The vehicle is 2 by 2 by 5 m long (6.5 by 6.5 by 15 ft), weighs 1360 kg (3000 lb) in air, and operates at submerged speeds to 1.5 m/sec (3 knots) and to depths of 760 m (2500 ft). The sensors include a Straza 500 active-passive sonar, acoustic altimeter, depthometer, compass, two Hydro Products television cameras with lights, and an EG&G 35-mm still camera with strobe. One major feature of all surface-powered vehicles is that their bottom time is only restricted by the time or ability of the surface support craft to stay on station.

The CURV II system consists of the vehicle, control cable, and control console. Although it normally operates from the YFNX-30 surface support ship, the system can be air-transported to operate from any surface ship of opportunity. It is primarily used for recovery of practice torpedoes from NOSC ranges.

Cable-Controlled Underwater Recovery Vehicle: CURV III. CURV III (Fig. 8-1), a more modern and deeper-depth version of the CURV II, is capable of operating in water depths of 2130 m (7000 ft). The CURV III system is comprised of the vehicle, control cable, and control console. Although it

Figure 8-1   Cable-controlled unmanned recovery vehicle, CURV III. (U.S. Navy.)

normally operates from the YFNX-30, the system is designed so that all major operational components can be disassembled, air-transported to a worksite, and installed on any surface craft that has adequate deck space. The vehicle normally carries a hydraulically operated claw for attaching and recovering items such as ordnance from the ocean floor. For special tasks, the claw is removed and replaced by a variety of grasping, cutting, or working tools. The vehicle also contains the necessary equipment for searching, locating, and documenting the lost item. Control of the vehicle and monitoring of the operations are done in the control van. The vehicle is 2 by 2 by 5 m long (6.5 by 6.5 by 15 ft) and weighs 2040 kg (4500 lb) in air. It normally operates to depths of 2130 m (7000 ft) but can be modified for emergency operations to 3050 m (10,000 ft). Its instrument suite includes a Straza 500 active-passive sonar with transponder integration capability, acoustic altimeter and depthometer, compass, two Hydro Products television cameras with lights, and an EG&G 35-mm still camera with strobe.

CURV III is a versatile underwater vehicle that can be readily modified to accommodate a wide variety of underwater tasks. It has demonstrated its search and recovery capabilities on the West Coast as well as in the Atlantic Ocean, most notably during the 1973 rescue of the PISCES III submersible off Ireland.

Remote Unmanned Work System (RUWS). Under the deep ocean technology (DOT) program, NOSC is developing RUWS, a remotely controlled submersible system that can perform a variety of work tasks at ocean depths to 6000 m (20,000 ft). This depth capability provides access to more than 98% of the ocean floor. The system is designed for air transport from specified ships of opportunity.

RUWS equipment on the support ship consists of a control center, motion compensation deck-handling system (MCDHS), diesel-power generators, and maintenance van. A single-coaxial-core, high-strength, synthetic cable connects the control center and the primary cable termination (PCT). The PCT serves as a line weight to aid on-station keeping and to limit forces that might otherwise be transmitted to the work vehicle. It is the power and signal distribution center between the primary cable and the flexible, multiconductor, vehicle tether. With its own propulsion system, it also provides the capability for ship-coordinated transit across the ocean floor to establish a new holding position.

The RUWS work vehicle (Fig. 8-2), which weighs 1950 kg (4300 lb) in air, is 1.4 by 1.4 by 3.4 m (4.5 by 4.5 by 11 ft). The work vehicle moves freely at the end of a buoyant flexible tether deployed from the PCT. Vehicle sensors include an active-passive CTFM sonar, bottom transponder inte-

Figure 8-2   Remote unmanned work system, RUWS. (U.S. Navy.)

grator, altimeter, depthometer, compass, head-coupled stereo television with lights, and EG&G 35-mm still camera with strobes. All signals and power needed to control and operate the submersible are multiplexed on the single coaxial core of the primary cable. A highly accurate, deep-ocean navigation system provides coordinated inputs to the vehicle's operators and the support ship's bridge.

The deep-ocean navigation system and a local-area, bottom-search sonar are used by the operator to guide the vehicle to the worksite. At the worksite a four-degree-of-freedom grabber holds the workpiece, while a highly dexterous, seven-degree-of-freedom manipulator positions individually powered tools or performs other work functions.

SNOOPY. SNOOPY is the smallest in a series of lightweight, portable, unmanned, undersea vehicle systems. Built as an experimental vehicle, it is capable of carrying a television camera with a 100-W, mercury vapor light source into the sea environment. As such, it can replace a diver for many tasks in which observation or surveillance is required. SNOOPY has two unique features: (1) all propulsion power is sent from the surface by hydraulic lines, and (2) an automatic depth-keeping capability is provided by a variable-buoyancy chamber and a depth feedback system. A small, electrically powered grabber is mounted on the forward end for implanting or retrieving lightweight objects. The vehicle is approximately 0.3 by 0.6 by 0.9 m long (1 by 2 by 3 ft), weighs 23 kg (50 lb) in air, and operates at speeds to 1 m/sec (2 knots) to depths of 30 m (100 ft).

ELECTRIC SNOOPY. ELECTRIC SNOOPY, the successor of SNOOPY, principally differs from its predecessor in its propulsion scheme. This experimental vehicle (see Fig. 9-15) uses three ¼-hp, oil-filled, pressure-balanced electric motors for thrust in the horizontal and vertical directions. This approach allows the use of a small-diameter 0.6-cm (¼-in.), 457-m (1500 ft), coaxial-tether cable. Alternating-current power, along with multiplexed control signals, is sent down the cable converted to variable, dc-motor-driven voltage through motor controllers. A single joystick controls forward, reverse, and turning motions. Twin pressure hulls house all vehicle electronics, a television camera, and a super-8 movie camera, all of which provide a streamlined and responsive vehicle. The super-8 camera provides intervals of action footage or a large number of individual-frame photographs. A single light provides illumination for both the television and film cameras. The vehicle is 0.5 by 0.6 by 0.9 m long (1.5 by 2.0 by 3.0 ft), weighs 68 kg (150 lb) in air, and operates to depths of 460 m (1500 ft).

When used in conjunction with a small buoyant reel, ELECTRIC SNOOPY has demonstrated that it can be used to attach a light line to a sea floor object, such as a stricken manned submersible, so that a heavy lift line with a "go-getter" can be guided to a hard point for surface lift.

NAVFAC SNOOPY. NAVFAC SNOOPY, shown in Figure 4-6, is a small, remotely controlled vehicle system that was designed and built for the Naval Facilities Engineering Command to support ocean construction work. Its primary uses are optical surveys of proposed undersea construction or implantment sites, surveillance and documentation of diver operations, and general undersea inspection and documentation. The vehicle is 0.6 by 0.6 by 1.2 m long (2 by 2 by 4 ft), weighs 135 kg (300 lb) in air, and operates to 460 m (1500 ft). It utilizes four hydraulically powered thrusters for horizontal and vertical excursions. The three horizontal thrusters are controlled by a three-axis, proportional joystick for integrated forward, reverse, turning, and lateral vehicle motions. The vertical thruster's control uses automatic depth- and altitude-holding circuitry with manual override. A low-light-level television camera with a 250 W, quartz iodized light is used for viewing, and a super-8 movie camera provides color documentation. Other sensors include a compass, altimeter, depthometer, and Straza 250 passive-active CTFM sonar. The vehicle's power, control signals, video signal, and instrument data are multiplexed onto a single coaxial tether.

Commercial and Academic Systems. In recent years, with the increased requirements of offshore industry, a number of unmanned undersea vehicles have been developed by industry, both in the United States and abroad. The following are typical examples of various types of commercial vehicles, with varying characteristics, each developed for specific needs.

Hydro Products RCV 225 and RCV 150.* Hydro Products, a Tetra Tech Company of San Diego, has developed and produced a number of unmanned remote-controlled underwater vehicles in two classes. The TCV 225 is a small basketball-shaped vehicle with four thrusters, lights, and a television camera. This 0.51-m (20-in.) diameter vehicle (Fig. 8-3) weighs 82 kg (180 lb) and by swimming on a short tether from a suspended "garage" can operate to depths of 2000 m (6600 ft). This type of system (more than eight such vehicles are in operation worldwide) is primarily used for offshore platform observation and inspection, pipeline inspection, bottom surveys, debris location, and observation of divers at work on critical tasks. The RCV 150 (Fig. 8-4) is a larger vehicle, about a 1.3-m (4.0-ft) cube that weighs approximately 450 kg (1000 lb). It, too, can operate to depths of 2000 m (6600 ft). In addition to thrusters, lights, and television, the RCV 150 has a four-function manipulator which, when outfitted with a selection of tools, can perform light underwater tasks. Its microcomputer-based control and display system facilitates addition of new tools, sensors, and advanced vehicle control concepts. It also continuously monitors vehicle performance so the operator is alerted to potential problem areas before they become serious. In addition to the tasks already described, the RCV 150 can be used

*RCV is a registered trademark of Hydro Products, Inc.

Figure 8-3   Remote-controlled vehicle, RCV 225. (Hydro Products, Inc.)

Figure 8-4   Remote-controlled vehicle, RCV 150. (Hydro Products, Inc.)

for removing debris, pulling or cutting cables, and emplacing, moving, or retrieving objects weighing up to 45 kg (100 lb) in water. Both the RCV 225 and RCV 150 are highly maneuverable with precise control; come with a full set of surface monitoring, control, and handling equipment; and are easily shipped from worksite to worksite.

Ametek Straza DEEP DRONE, SCORPIO, and SCARAB.   The Straza Division of the Ametek Corporation has developed, and delivered to users in the deep sea, a family of three unmanned cable-controlled undersea vehicles. These vehicles, based on the U.S. Navy's CURV-type configuration, are designed to perform work on the sea floor. The DEEP DRONE (Fig. 8-5), built for the U.S. Navy's Supervisor of Salvage, is about 1.3 by 1.3 by 1.8 m (4 by 4 by 6 ft), weighs about 2270 kg (5000 lb) and can operate to depths of 610 m (2000 ft) in currents up to 1.5 m/sec (3 knots). It is equipped with a television camera, a film camera with associated lights, and a high-resolution Straza model 250 CTFM sonar. It is utilized for search, inspection, and recovery of items lost at sea. The SCORPIO (Fig. 8-6) is 1.2 by 1.6 by 2.2 m (4 by 5.3 by 7.3 ft), weighs about 680 kg (1500 lb), and operates to depths of 915 m (3000 ft) in currents up to 1.5 m/sec (3 knots). It has four 15-hp hydraulic thrusters and automatic depth and heading control. It has a 360° scanning CTFM sonar and acoustic beacon receiver, a television camera with water-corrected lens and lights on a 180° pan and tilt unit, plus a five-motion manipulator with 91-kg (200 lb) lift capability. SCORPIO is used for location, inspection, and recovery of underwater equipment; sea floor surveys; observation of undersea operations; and various other undersea work tasks. The SCARAB system is designed to assist with inspection and repair of sub-merged telephone cables. It will locate, unbury, attach, cut, recover, and rebury a malfunctioning cable in a minimum amount of time at depths to 1830 m (6000 ft). The total system, including electrical power supplies, launching equipment, operator's hut, and vehicle, is completely self-contained and can operate from selected ships of opportunity. The entire system, weighing approximately 36,500 kg (80,000 lb) is transportable by standard air cargo aircraft. The SCARAB undersea vehicle is about 1.3 by 1.6 by 2.1 m (4 by 5 by 7 ft) and weighs 2270 kg (5000 lb).

Remote Ocean Systems TELESUB 1000.   Remote Ocean Systems, Inc. of San Diego has produced an economical, high-performance, highly versatile, small, remotely controlled undersea vehicle (Fig. 8-7). The TELESUB 1000 is 0.8 m (31 in.) wide by 0.2 m (27 in.) high by 1.4 m (55 in.) in length. It weighs just 250 kg (550 lb) and operates to depths of 610 m (2000 ft). Its three 1-hp horizontal thrusters, two forward-aft and one transverse, provide high maneuverability and a maximum speed of 1.2 m/sec (2.3 knots).

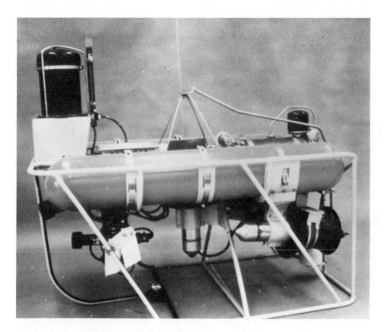

Figure 8-5   DEEP DRONE. (Ametek Straza.)

Figure 8-6   SCORPIO. (Ametek Straza.)

89

Figure 8-7   TELESUB. (Remote Oceans Systems, Inc.)

Vehicle sensors include a wide-angle television camera, two 500-W in-candescent lights, a magnetic compass, and a depthometer. It features simple joystick controls and an automatic depth and heading lock. It is used for underwater observation, inspection, and simple underwater tasks such as implantment and recovery of small objects and cutting of lines and cables.

Perry Oceanographics RECON II, III, IV, V.   Perry Oceanographics, Inc. of Riviera Beach, Florida has been in the forefront in producing versatile, practical manned submersibles. With literally dozens of their submersibles in operation worldwide, the management at Perry, concerned with safety of operations, decided to produce a small unmanned vehicle that could be fabricated and operated at low cost and could be made available in areas of manned submersible operation. This vehicle would be able to rapidly deploy and be capable of attaching lifting lines to a distressed submersible to effect rescue. Via the U.S. Navy technology transfer program, Perry engineers contacted the NOSC for design and performance data on the SNOOPY vehicles to use as background for their development. As the Perry engineers developed their own design and added their innovations, a new class of small unmanned vehicles emerged that found many missions beyond the original rescue intent. The RECON II is an undersea vehicle that weighs 280 kg (620 lb), is 1.2 by 0.9 by 0.9 m (4 by 3 by 3 ft), and operates to depths of 460 m (1500 ft). It carries a television camera and lights and a simple manipulator and has a 45-kg (100 lb) payload capability. RECON III (Fig. 8-8) is a simpler, lighter-weight vehicle of 140 kg (308 lb) with a depth capability of 183 m (600 ft). The vehicle is 1.4 by 0.71 by 0.61 m (56 by 28 by 24 in.) in size and has an optional payload of 11 kg (24 lb). It has three reversible electric thrusters, two fore- and aft-oriented and one vertically oriented for depth control. It carries a television camera and light on a tilt mechanism and a magnetic compass and depth pressure transducer. Control is by a simple joystick. RECON IV is a larger and heavier 412 kg (900-lb) work vehicle with a deeper diving capability of 1530 m (5000 ft). This vehicle, 1.5 by 1.2 by 1.2 m (5 by 4 by 3.8 ft), carries a television camera and lights, hydraulic system for the three thrusters, and a manipulator. The manipulator has a hydraulically operated two-fingered claw with 90° rotation, 0.35-m (14-in.) extension, and 0.1-m (4-in.) claw aperture. Cutter heads and various other jaws can be interchanged. This vehicle can carry out fairly sophisticated tasks and can be applied to a variety of undersea missions. RECON V (Fig. 8-9) is a streamlined, teardrop-shaped, 227-kg (500 lb) vehicle designed to operate to 366-m (1200-ft) depths. It is approxi-

Figure 8-8   RECON III. (Perry Oceanographics, Inc.)

Figure 8-9   RECON V. (Perry Oceanographics, Inc.)

mately 1.75 by 0.91 by 1.0 m (70 by 36 by 39 in.) in size. Its electro-hydraulic power system drives five reversible thrusters, two fore- and aft-oriented, two vertically oriented, and one of transverse orientation. This provides precise maneuverability. It carries a television camera and light on a pan and tilt mechanism with a 270° pan and 90° tilt. There is provision for a second camera as needed. It also carries a magnetic compass and depth pressure transducer, with an acoustic beacon and navigation system optional. A manipulator similar to the one described for RECON IV is provided. Each of the RECON vehicles is fabricated with an aluminum frame with a glass-reinforced plastic upper body covering and is equipped with flotation material to provide a net positive buoyancy when underwater. The vertical thrusters drive them down and maintain depth control, and they will surface due to their own buoyancy should a power failure occur. In addition, each system includes an integrated surface control center, power supplies, handling equipment, and an umbilical cable and winch. This series of small lightweight undersea vehicles provides an easily deployable capability to immediately deal with emergency situations or to perform more exacting undersea tasks.

ISE TROV and TREC.   International Submarine Engineering Ltd. of Port Moody, British Columbia, Canada has developed and is producing a family of remotely controlled undersea work vehicles. As of this writing, 10 TROV (tethered remotely operated vehicle) systems have been built and delivered to a variety of customers. This vehicle weighs 720-kg (1600-lb) is 2.1 by 1.3 by 1.3-m (7 by 4.2 by 4.2 ft), and has an operating depth to 370 m (1200 ft).

Figure 8-10   TREC. (International Submarine Engineering, Ltd.)

The vehicle comprises a rectangular frame on which are mounted two 5-hp electric motors that power horizontal propellers and one each of 5-hp electric motors powering a lateral and a vertical propeller, two hydraulic back-hoe type manipulators, four 0.3-m- (1-ft-) diameter by 1.5-m (5-ft) long syntactic foam flotation cylinders, one air ballast tank, two pressure-compensated logic and power chambers, and a suite of sensors. The sensors include three 1500-W external lights, a strobe, an echo sounder, a pinger, and a television camera. The TREC vehicles (Fig. 8-10), of which nine have been built and delivered, are similar in general arrangement to the TROV but smaller in size. These 19 vehicles are finding extensive use, in supporting undersea work, throughout the world.

Scripps Marine Physical Laboratory RUM. The remote underwater manipulator (RUM) was developed at the Marine Physical Laboratory (MPL) at Scripps Institute of Oceanography (SIO) in La Jolla, California. It is a tracked vehicle capable of operating along the seabed to depths of 2450 m (8000 ft) like a Caterpillar tractor. It is 5.5 by 2.7 by 3.4 m (18.5 by 9 by 11 ft) in size and weighs 11,000 kg (24,000 lb). It is equipped with a manipulator with six degrees of movement plus grip capable of exerting 23-kg (50-lb) force or lifting up to 455 kg (1000 lb) using a single hook. The RUM is instrumented as follows: eight external lights, an echo sounder, a sonar, a pinger, a still color camera, two television cameras, and a movie camera. It normally operates via its tether to its special support platform ORB (oceanographic research buoy), a 12 × 12 m (40 × 40 ft) square barge with a center well. The RUM/ORB system usually operates in support of the SIO/MPL oceanographic research programs.

European Systems. In recent years, many additional missions, both commercial and research, have expanded the interest in utilizing unmanned undersea work systems. Many have been developed and are in operation worldwide, especially in the North Sea oil and gas fields. The following are some representative European-developed systems.

BAC CONSUB I and II. Engineers at Electronic and Space Systems, a part of British Aerospace Dynamics Group, in Bristol, England have developed two undersea vehicles: the CONSUB I and CONSUB II. Their first unmanned submersible, CONSUB I, was built as a research vehicle for the Institute of Geological Sciences and entered service in 1974. CONSUB II was completed in the summer of 1977. This 2950 kg (6500-lb) vehicle is 3.7 by 2.1 by 1.7 m (12 by 7 by 5.5 ft) and operates to a maximum depth of 600 m (2000 ft). With its four 12.5-hp thrusters, CONSUB II can stem a 3-knot current near the surface and a 2-knot current down to its maximum working depth. The robust box framework is constructed from corrosion-resistant aluminum tubing. Buoyancy is provided by syntactic foam blocks. A heavy-duty pan and tilt unit is mounted forward in the center of the framework and is capable of carrying a payload of 41 kg (90 lb) dry and rotating through ±190° at a rate of 3 rpm. A television system is fitted as standard, with both still and movie cameras as optional equipment. Nine 1-kW lights provide illumination for both the video and photo requirements. A depth gauge, magnetic compass, flasher unit, and emergency sonar beacon complete the outfitting of the vehicle. The 1.3 cm (0.5 in.) diameter umbilical cable is a multiconductor composite including a 6000-kg (13,000-lb) breaking strain, KEVLAR core, three RG58/BU coax, and 12 twisted pair and 15 power conductors. A versatile system, COBSUB II will not only perform site surveys and inspection but also assist in installation and repair of equipment and geological, geophysical, and marine surveys.

Figure 8-11   ANGUS 001. (Heriot-Watt University.)

HWU ANGUS 001, 002, 003. The Underwater Technology Group at Heriot-Watt University in Edinburgh, Scotland has developed a series of unmanned cable-controlled submersibles called ANGUS, which stands for "a navigable general-purpose underwater surveyor." Three units have been built. The first, ANGUS 001 (Fig. 8-11), was fabricated from parts from a British Navy MK 30 torpedo. It operated successfully for a couple of years but has now been retired from operational service. ANGUS 002 and 003 are similar in configuration, with 003 being slightly larger and having more powerful thrusters. They both operate to 300-m (1000-ft) depths. ANGUS 002 (Fig. 8-12) is a rectangular vehicle 2.3 by 1.3 by 1.2 m (8 by 4.2 by 4 ft) weighing 700 kg (1650 lb), with a speed of 1.5 knots, measured with 200 m (650 ft) of cable deployed. It has two 4.5-hp vertical thrusters. The payload includes a television camera, a super-8 movie camera, a 35-mm still camera, and two 650-W quartz halogen lights. Undersea navigation is provided by a long-baseline acoustic system. ANGUS 003 is similar to 002 except it weighs 1000 kg (2200 lb), has a speed of 3.5 knots (surface) and 2.0 knots at 300 m (600 ft) and has larger thrusters. These vehicles have performed well on many sea trials, supporting survey, inspection, and

Figure 8-12   ANGUS 002. (Heriot-Watt University.)

search and recovery operations. The long-term aim of this university project is to study "in depth" all the problems associated with unmanned, remotely controlled submersibles for fundamental scientific and engineering knowledge. The output of the ANGUS project will benefit all who desire to build vehicles that will work within the sea.

CERTSM ERIC I and II.   The ERIC I (Engin de Recherche et d'Intervention a Cable) is an unmanned cable-powered submersible craft developed for survey and research work by the French Navy at the Centre d'Etude et de Recherches Techniques Sous-Marine (CERTSM) in Toulon, France. This vehicle is 4 by 2 by 2 m (13 by 6.5 by 6.5 ft), weighs 2800 kg (6272 lb) in air, and has a maximum operating depth of 600 m (2000 ft). The three electric propulsion motors, buoyancy tanks, sensors, and working tools are mounted on an open framework. The sensors include six 400-W lights, two television cameras, a cinecamera, an echo sounder, a sonar, and a pinger. ERIC I carries a hydraulic dexterous manipulator with five degrees of movement and a claw that is 0.15 m (6 in.) in length and has a 0.15-m (6-in.) aperture. Its emergency features include a marker buoy with line and flashing beacon. The ERIC II is currently under development at CERTSM. The ERIC II vehicle (fish) is designed to operate from a deeply suspended garage (PAGODE) and in conjunction with a deep-towed photographic survey fish (PARC). The ERIC II is planned to be a streamlined, hydrodynamically shaped vehicle of 5 by 3 by 1.8 m (16.4 by 10 by 5.0 ft) weighing 4550 kg (10,000 lb) with an operating depth of 8000 m (26,000 ft). The propulsion will be provided by six drive units in tunnels and used for controlling six degrees of movement of the vehicle. This vehicle will have two manipulators and lights, television cameras, cinecamera, sonar, echo sounder, and gyrocompass.

The PARC-ERIC II systems is an integrated deep-water system, for exploration, systematic search, and intervention, remotely operated from a surface ship. Depending on the missions involved and the equipment carried, the ship may deploy PARC for exploration or search or ERIC II for finer search and intervention. This development requires basic equipment common to both systems as well as equipment specific to each of them. The common basic equipment, carried whatever the mission in view, consists of the acoustic navigation, the towing cable with power and data transmission equipment, the technical shelter, the cable- and fish-handling equipment, and the electric generator units. In addition, the ship must have a heave and attitude platform and, if possible, a satellite navigation system. PARC is basically designed for systematic photographic surveying of the seabed with the following specific elements: the PARC fish, which carries the sensors (photographic equipment, television, sounder, pressure sensor, navigation transponder, etc.); the illuminator, which weights down the cable and overhangs the PARC fish by an adjustable height and, if necessary, carries a side-looking sonar; the navigation and real-time data exploitation shelter; and the photographic development, processing, and filming shelter. ERIC II is designed for detailed exploration and remote intervention by teleoperation with the following specific elements: the PAGODE fish, which weights down the cable, stores the tether cable, and is used as a handling system for ERIC II; the self-propelled teleoperator ERIC II fish, which carries active elements (propellers, TV cameras, teleoperator arms, panoramic sonar, heading and attitude platform, navigation transponder, etc.); and the control and navigation shelter. The transition between the PARC configuration and the ERIC II configuration is obtained by changing software in the technical shelter, by attaching one fish or another to the towing cable end, and by connecting the specific shelter with the technical shelter. The development of complex, innovative, highly capable systems requires considerable improvement in basic technology, and it will be interesting to monitor this system's fabrication and initial deployment.

CSI SNURRE.   The SNURRE is an unmanned cable-powered submersible craft developed in Norway for the Continental Shelf Institute (CSI) by the Central Institute for Industrial Research, Det Norske Veritas, and A/S Hydrauli-

control. It is an open-frame vehicle of 2.3 by 1.8 by 1.6 m (7.5 by 6 by 5.2 ft) weighing 960 kg (2100 lb) in air and having an operating depth of 500 m (1640 ft). Mobility is provided by four 5-hp hydraulic motors powering three horizontal propellers, with a 120° separation in angle of attack, and one vertical propeller—all controlled by an all-directional joystick control. It carries four 250-W lights plus a flash for still photography, two television cameras, a cinecamera, an echo sounder, a sonar, a pinger, two still cameras, and a 182-kg (400-lb) lift-capability manipulator. It is further outfitted with a cone penetrometer and vane shear capable of measuring continuously to 3 m (9.9 ft) below the sea floor surface.

Unmanned Towed Vehicles

Towed systems comprise a class of tethered unmanned undersea vehicles that, while they cannot stop and perform "work" on the sea floor, are still valuable contributors of data to determine site locations and conditions and to survey work areas between operations. These vehicles do not have thrusters of their own but operate on a trajectory dictated by the speed and length of tow tether and dynamic forces of control surfaces, such as rudders, elevators, etc. These systems are usually equipped with side-looking sonars, still cameras, and sometimes slow-scan television, along with a forward-looking obstacle avoidance sonar and depth and height-off-the-bottom measuring devices. During operations, these vehicles, commonly called "fishes," are towed just off the bottom at an altitude set by the characteristics of the primary sensors and in straight lines along perdetermined courses. The following are the characteristics of a representative sample of this type of vehicle.

Scripps Institute of Oceanography DEEP TOW. The DEEP TOW vehicles (Fig. 8-13) are cylindrical in shape with pipe runners for protection in case of impact with the sea floor. They are about 0.8 by 1.3 by 3 m (2.5 by 4.2 by 10 ft) in size and weigh 1100 kg (2450 lb). They are designed to operate to depths to 6000 m (20,000 ft). The tether winch handles tow wire of at least 1½ times water depth in length, with winding speed of up to 47 m/min (161 ft/min). DEEP TOW usually carries a stroboscopic light, an echo sounder, a sonar, a still color camera, and a television camera.

U.S. Naval Oceanographic Office TELEPROBE. The TELEPROBE is an open framework on which sensors are mounted and dynamic control surfaces installed. Its size is about 1.2 by 1.7 by 3 m (4 by 5.5 by 10 ft), and it weighs 1600 kg (3600 lb). It can operate to depths of 6000 m (20,000 ft) from a tether handling winch with 9000 m (30,000 ft) of tow line. It is instrumented with a sonar, a pinger, two still cameras, and a television camera. The television capability is limited to 3000-m (10,000-ft) operations due to the data bandwidth of the tether cable.

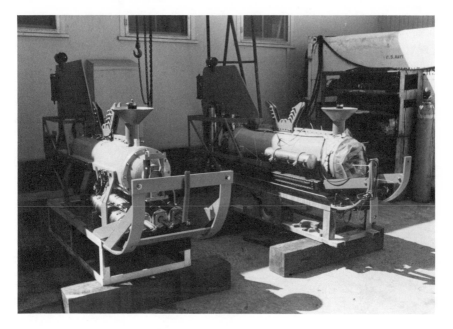

Figure 8-13   DEEP TOW. (Scripps Institution of Oceanography.)

Unmanned Free-Swimming Vehicles

A third class of unmanned undersea vehicles is exemplified by the free-swimming untethered vehicles developed by the Applied Physics Laboratory at the University of Washington in Seattle, Washington. Similar in mission to the towed vehicles, these free swimmers do not stop and perform "work" but do collect valuable data in a very efficient way. Each of these vehicles is cylindrical (torpedo-shaped) and carries an independent power source, its own navigation system, as well as a variety of sensors and a tape recorder for the collected data. The SPURV I and II (self-propelled underwater research vehicle) are each about 0.6 by 0.6 by 3 m (2 by 2 by 10 ft), weigh 455 kg (1000 lb) and can carry a payload of 45 kg (100 lb). The SPURV I can operate to a 365-m (1200-ft) depth and the SPURV II to 1800 m (6000 ft). They each have a 5- to 6-hr endurance at speeds of 4–6 knots. The UARS (unmanned Arctic research submersible) (Fig. 8-14) is similar to the SPURV vehicles except it is about 0.5 by 0.5 by 3 m (1.5 by 1.5 by 10 ft) and weighs 410 kg (900 lb), with a 22-kg (50-lb) payload. It carries a sonar, a pinger, and an acoustic homing system for return to the launch hole when operating under the Arctic ice pack.

The Naval Ocean Systems Center (NOSC) has developed a robot-type test-bed submersible, known simply as the FREE SWIMMER (Fig. 4-7), with

Figure 8-14   Unmanned Arctic research submersible (UARS). (Applied Physics Laboratory.)

which to demonstrate new, improved vehicle system technologies. The submersible is 0.5 by 0.5 by 3 m (1.7 by 1.7 by 9 ft). It is of modular construction, which provides for expansion to accommodate additional payloads and new sensor systems as demonstration for those technologies becomes feasible. The vehicle is designed to follow a set of preprogrammed tracks such as a parallel-path search or a figure-eight demonstration run. In this mode of operation, the vehicle is programmed via a computer console and an umbilical cable which is disconnected after the initial preprogramming phase. The vehicle is then allowed to follow this course until it completes its mission. If an emergency arises, automatic procedures allow the vehicle to turn on an emergency beacon and shut off all thrusters, and then the reserve buoyancy allows it to return to the surface. After initial tests in this operating mode, other methods of vehicle command control and communications will be demonstrated. Among these are an acoustic control link, an acoustic slow-scan television link, and an expendable fiber optics duplex communication link. The end product will be a system that can perform rudimentary tasks, such as search, inspection, and pipeline surveys, without direct operator control, free of cable drag and cable-handling problems.

Diver's Systems

The most common means of extending human work capability into the sea is by outfitting people in diving equipment. While divers are restricted in the undersea environment by pressure, temperature, and communications, they can make use directly of their hands, eyes, ears, and the mobility of their limbs. For shallow operations in a friendly environment, divers can perform many useful complex functions. There are many books and excellent articles on the history, status, and limitations of diving, so only the generic types of diving systems will be described here. These are the swimmer, scuba, hard hat, saturation, and 1-atm diving systems.

Swimmer. The unequipped swimmer is the simplest means for humans to work within the sea. While limited to very shallow depths [usually less than 7.6 m (25 ft) and very short dive duration (usually less than 3 min)], this is a very inexpensive means to perform routine tasks. Simple visual search and recovery of lost objects and repetitive functions, such as pearl harvesting, have used surface diving by swimmers for centuries.

Scuba. With the invention of the scuba (self-contained underwater breathing apparatus) by Jacques Cousteau, a whole new dimension of undersea exploration and work capability was opened. The diver (Fig. 8-15) could now stay down for extended periods (dependent on time and depth), relatively unencumbered by a set of lightweight equipment. Depths to 40 m (130 ft) for routine diving and the possibility of excursions to 60 m (200 ft) or even 26 m (250 ft) were attainable. With the wet suit to ward off the undersea chill and scuba gear, divers can perform a wide variety of undersea tasks and become, themselves, the major part of an undersea work system.

Hard Hat. Hard hat divers are more heavily encumbered with equipment than scuba divers, but they have direct power, communications, and breathing gas supply connections to their tending vessel. This tethered mode of operation is important for many types of difficult tasks in dangerous, low-visibility conditions and where power assist tools are required. The hard hat divers can operate routinely to 60 m (200 ft) and deeper with reduced time on scene, according to the criticalness of the need and paid for by the very long decompression times.

Saturation. Saturation diving was developed to provide long-term excursions on the deep sea floor with no immediate decompression after each individual dive. Basically, it involves compressing divers, within pressure chambers, to the equivalent pressure of the sea depth into which they will operate. Then with scuba or tethered gas supply, divers are transported via a

Figure 8-15 Divers in scuba gear. (U.S. Navy.)

pressurized bell to the operating depth where they exit into the sea and perform their work without regard to time. Upon completion of a dive, divers reenter the pressurized bell and, without a change in pressure, are transported back to the base pressure chamber (on the deck of the tending vessel). As long as the pressure does not change, divers can work long hours during each excursion and make multiple excursions, with just one long decompression upon the completion of operations. This long decompression from a saturation mode of operations is roughly one 24-hr period per 30 m (100 ft) of depth. Saturation diving requires special gas mixtures very closely controlled during all phases of the operation. When helium is substituted for the nitrogen of air, the heat loss from a diver's body must be closely controlled, and communication difficulties must be overcome due to the "Donald Duck" effect of "helium" speech. There are good books on the physiology and psychology of saturation diving, so suffice it to say here that this concept provides an important means to conduct undersea work to depths in excess of 300 m (1000 ft), and possibly to depths of 1000 m (3000 ft) in the future. There are many commercial as well as U.S. Navy saturation diving systems available to support undersea work. These systems (Fig. 8-16) usually consist of a large cylindrical *deck decompression chamber* (DDC) for the long-term support of about four divers and a smaller

Figure 8-16   U.S. Navy MK II saturation diving system. (U.S. Navy.)

personnel transfer chamber (PTC) that may be docked to the DDC, allowing a two-person diving team to enter the PTC while under pressure, and then undocked and the PTC lowered to the operating depth. The two-diver team usually operates from the PCT on tethers to the worksite. The control consoles and gas supply make up the remainder of the system.

One-Atmosphere (1-atm).   A final means to put man into the sea as a diver is with a 1-atm suit. This type of system employs a high-strength pressure-resistant suit to maintain the diver in a dry nonpressurized environment. Armored suits have been tried for many years, but usually the weight and stiffness of joints have negated the potential advantages of eliminating both decompression and special gas mixtures. Recently, significant break-

Figure 8-17   One-atmosphere diving suit, JIM. (Oceaneering International.)

throughs in both design and application of materials have allowed the production of a practical lightweight system with flexible joints. DHB Construction Ltd of Alton, England has developed a series of suits called JIM and SAM. These suits can operate to depths of 460 m (1500 ft) for unlimited time since the operator (diver) is protected from the external pressure. The JIM suits (Fig. 8-17) weigh 500 kg (1100 lb) in air and are slightly negative in water to allow the diver to walk on the sea floor, climb ladders, and perform work in a normal gravitational environment. Its small size relative to submersibles operating to these depths, lack of decompression relative to saturation diving systems, and ease of logistics for quick transport and setup make the 1-atm suit a viable system to use for many undersea work tasks.

Manned Submersibles

The ability to take humans to the sea floor in a 1-atm "shirt-sleeve" environment, in order to directly observe and perform work, has been one of the great achievements over the last three decades. The pioneering work by Dr. Auguste Piccard with the development of the original TRIESTE bathyscaph and by Captain Jacques Cousteau with the diving saucer (sous coupe) initiated a new means of exploration of the undersea world. Much has been written on the development and operations of manned submersibles, and several fine documents have been written that present their characteristics (see the Bibliography of this chapter). Therefore, no attempt will be made to create a total inventory listing. Rather, the particular characteristics of a few generic classes of submersibles will be described along with their specialized capabilities.

To better understand the depths of the world's oceans, the U.S. Navy has long recognized the need for deep-diving submersibles to carry out missions of search, rescue, and investigation. As such, it has assisted in the development of submersibles that run the gamut from midocean depths to 6100 m (20,000 ft), thereby providing access to approximately 98% of the ocean floor.

The ALVIN, developed by General Mills, Inc. of Minneapolis, Minnesota and operated for the U.S. Navy by the Woods Hole Oceanographic

Figure 8-18   ALVIN. (U.S. Navy.)

Institute, is a particularly fine example of a craft built for undersea research and experimentation. Recently modified with the replacement of the original steel personnel hull with one of titanium, this submersible (Fig. 8-18) [7 by 2.6 by 3.8 m (22.5 by 8.5 by 12.5 ft)] now has a depth capability of 3500 m (11,500 ft). This 14,500-kg (32,000-lb) boat can carry one pilot and two observers—for dives normally scheduled for up to an 8-hr duration, with an additional 64 hr of emergency life support endurance available. The pressure hull has four forward-looking viewports and one small viewport in the top hatch. It carries an electrically powered, dropable manipulator that has six degrees of motion, a 23-kg (50-lb) lift capacity, a 1.9-m (63-in.) maximum extension, and a scissor-type claw with attachments for simple collection and light coring work. ALVIN is highly maneuverable with an articulated main 7.5-hp thruster that swings horizontally and two pivotable 2-hp thrusters located amidships. Sensor equipment includes external lights, still cameras, television cameras, an echo sounder, a sonar, a pinger, and an underwater telephone. Emergency features include releasable batteries and, unique to the ALVIN, a releasable personnel sphere. Its 680-kg (1500-lb) payload makes ALVIN a powerful undersea research and work tool.

TURTLE and SEACLIFF, operated by Submarine Development Group One, San Diego, California, are identical in design and operation and are two of the U.S. Navy's versatile, deep-diving research submersibles (Fig. 8-19).

Figure 8-19   SEACLIFF. (U.S. Navy.)

Having a depth capability of 2000 m (6500 ft), these self-propelled vehicles are designed for search, work, recovery, and exploration, being similar in appearance to ALVIN. Each is 8 m (26 ft) long and weighs approximately 20,000 kg (43,000 lb). Primary power is provided by lead-acid batteries. Designed to operate at a maximum depth for sustained periods of time, each vehicle with its crew of three can maneuver underwater for approximately 10 hr at a speed of 1.5 knots while conducting normal search operations. Navigation equipment provides personnel in the sphere with such information as depth above and below the vehicle, speed, distance covered, and true compass readings. The vehicles are fitted with a sonar system, an underwater telephone, and a radio communications system. Equipment designed to enhance mission capabilities includes closed-circuit television, transparent viewports, and lights for illuminating the area around the vehicle and the ocean floor. The vehicles are also fitted with a pair of articulated arms, or manipulators, that have a complement of tools for cutting, drilling, and grasping. Mounted on the forward end of the vehicle between the manipulators are baskets that can hold tools as well as small objects recovered from the ocean floor.

The deep-submergence rescue vehicle (DSRV) (Fig. 8-20) is a deep-diving submersible designed to dock on the hatch of a disabled submarine and take aboard the submarine's personnel. The DSRV weighs approximately

Figure 8-20   Deep-submergence rescue vehicle, DSRV. (U.S. Navy.)

Figure 8-21   TRIESTE II. (U.S. Navy.)

29,500 kg (65,000 lb) in air and has a displacement of 34,500 kg (76,000 lb) when submerged. It is powered by silver-zinc batteries and has a maximum speed of 4.5 knots. It has an operating time of 10 hr at cruise speed with a 30% reserve power supply. Maximum operating depth is 1500 m (5000 ft). The DSRV can be launched either from a "mother" submarine or from an ASR 21 class submarine rescue ship. During a rescue mission, the vehicle and its support equipment can be loaded on aircraft for "fly away" to a port nearest the disaster area. There the vehicle can be loaded on either a "mother" submarine or an ASR for the rescue operation. The DSRV, through its many sensing devices, can locate the disabled submarine, dock on either the forward or the after hatch, and take aboard 24 of the sub's crew on each trip for transfer to the support craft. Two such vehicles are in operation under cognizance of the Submarine Development Group One, San Diego, California. The vehicles were developed by Lockheed Missiles and Space Co. under the direction of the U.S. Naval Ships Systems Command.

TRIESTE, the U.S. Navy's deepest-diving vehicle, is capable of carrying three people on scientific, search, and recovery missions to depths of 6100 m (20,000 ft) (Fig. 8-21). In 1960, TRIESTE dove to 11,000 m (35,800 ft) in the Mariana Trench. The operating concept of TRIESTE is described in Chapter 4. The three-person 1.8-m (6-ft) diameter pressure sphere is supported by a large gasoline-filled float, bringing the total dimensions of this

Figure 8-22   NEMO. (U.S. Navy.)

82,000-kg (180,000 lb) craft to 24 by 5.8 by 8.3 m (78.5 by 18.8 by 27 ft).
TRIESTE is outfitted with a search sonar, manipulators, and a photographic
suite.

Small, agile submersibles with panoramic visibility have been found to
be ideal vehicles for carrying people and equipment on reconnaissance and
sea floor missions in the ocean. Recognizing this fact, NOSC has pursued
programs for demonstration of new technology in their design, fabrication,
and utilization. The products of these programs are several systems that
differ in concept, structural materials, mobility, and applications. However,
with the least investment in size and complexity of supporting equipment,
they all provide the user with underwater panoramic visibility.

The naval experimental manned observatory (NEMO) (Fig. 8-22) is a
self-contained submersible with a 1-atm environment. The vehicle has been
U.S. Navy-certified for an operating depth to 180 m (600 ft) and carries a

crew of two (an operator and an observer). In addition to the crew, the vehicle can carry a payload of 210 kg (450 lb). The pressure hull is constructed from acrylic plastic and has an outside diameter of 1.8 m (66 in.) with a wall thickness of 6.3 cm (2.5 in.). (See Chap. 5 on acrylic pressure hull development.) The spherical hull is supported by a structural cage. The cage serves two functions: It supports the weight of NEMO and also provides a shield which protects the acrylic sphere from impact loads. Directly below the cage is a unit containing the main ballast tank, service module, and main battery pack. The vehicle has several modes of operation. It can take on ballast and make a free descent or can drop its anchor and winch itself down. Because of this self-contained anchor and winch system, the NEMO can hover in the water column at any depth with low power consumption. The vehicle has a vertical speed of 10 to 20 m/min (30-60 ft/min) and a life support system of 64 workhours. NEMO was developed by the Civil Engineering Laboratory (CEL), Port Hueneme, California.

MAKAKAI, a transparent hull submersible, is a two-person, free-swimming submersible developed and built by NOSC. The vehicle (Fig. 8-23) has been U.S. Navy-certified for an operational depth of 180 m (600 ft). It utilizes a NEMO-type acrylic sphere as the pressure hull; this affords the operator and the passenger an unobstructed, panoramic view of the outside surroundings. The pressure hull is mounted on a frame to which

Figure 8-23 MAKAKAI. (U.S. Navy.)

Figure 8-24   JOHNSON-SEALINK II. (Harbor Branch Foundation, Inc.)

two pontoons are secured. The pontoons house the lead-acid batteries used for the power supply. Each pontoon contains tanks that are used for ballast and trim during diving operations. MAKAKAI is propelled by two sets of oppositely arranged, cycloidal-thrust units which provide a cruising speed of 0.5–0.75 knot with a maximum speed of 3 knots. In addition, the thrusters provide four degrees of freedom for the vehicle by altering the pitch of the propeller blades. The vehicle has a payload of 400 kg (870 lb) including the crew and can support a mission of 8-hr duration. MAKAKAI is presently on loan to Sea World, Inc.

Additional applications of the U.S. Navy transparent hull technology are the JOHNSON-SEALINK I and II submersibles, developed and operated by the Harbor Branch Foundation, Inc. in Fort Pierce, Florida. Mr. Ed. Link, long an innovator of electromechanical systems, purchased NEMO-type acrylic hulls that were then mounted on a tubular aluminum frame along with a diving lockout chamber to provide a versatile undersea vehicle. The two submersibles (Fig. 8-24) are certified by the American Bureau of Shipping (ABS) for operations to 300 m (1000 ft). These 10,000 kg (23,000 lb) submersibles are 7 by 2.4 by 3.3 (22.9 by 8 by 10.7 ft) in size. They can cruise at 0.75 knot and have a maximum speed of 1.75 knots. They are outfitted with a six-function manipulator, sonar, doppler navigator, underwater telephone, and still, movie, and video camera systems with associated lights. The life support of breathing gases and carbon dioxide scrubbers provide an emergency endurance of 480 workhours (20 workdays). High maneuverability is provided by use of a combination of two vertical, one transverse, two side, and three aft steerable thrusters. The

Figure 8-25   SUPERSUB I, PC 1803. (Perry Oceanographics, Inc.)

combination of panoramic visibility for the pilots and a diver's lock-out system make these submersibles most capable undersea research and engineering systems.

Two manufacturers have provided most of the working manned submersibles in the commercial field. By concentrating on ruggedness, reliability, and minimizing costs, the Perry Submarine Builders of Riviera Beach, Florida and Hyco (International Hydrodynamics Co., Ltd.) in North Vancouver, British Columbia, Canada, have developed leadership in the field.

Perry PC Series Submersibles.   The Perry boats are modular in construction and are easily recognized by the 0.9–1.2-m (3–4-ft) diameter cylindrical shape with a small conning tower and four horizontal viewports and one vertical viewport (Fig. 8-25). They have large-diameter (approximately 140° included angle) acrylic viewports in the bow to provide unobstructed panoramic visibility. The lengths vary from 6 to 10 m (20–33 ft) depending on the mission of the craft. The shorter craft are primarily workboats designed for operation by a crew of two to depths of 360 m (1200 ft) for the PC-14 to 910 m (3000 ft) for the PC-16. The longer boats include a diver lock-out capability and operate to depths of 200 m (660 ft) for the PC-18 series and 460 m (1500 ft) for the PC-15. Perry has built many submersibles from the early Cubmarines to the PC-18 series, sometimes with three or four specially tailored craft as slight modifications within one model series (e.g., PC 1201 and 1202 to 1205 and PC 1801, 1802, etc.). These boats are of modular construction to provide flexibility in configuration and have modular electrical systems, dry battery pods with quick-change trays, a full set of instrumentation, sensors, lights, cameras, manipulators, and navigation/communication equipment that may be installed to accommodate the particular mission requirements.

HYCO PISCES Submersibles. The 12 PISCES manned submersibles built by International Hydrodynamics Company Ltd. (HYCO) have a unique exterior shape with the manned sphere forward with a "brow" of buoyancy material and a streamlined hydrodynamic shape faired in behind the sphere. These 12 boats range in operating depths from 350 m (1100 ft) for PISCES I, to 2500 m (8300 ft) for PISCES VI and IX, and 2000 m (6600 ft) for PISCES IV, V, VII, and XI. A typical craft, the PISCES IV, is 6.1 by 3 by 3.7 m (20 by 10 by 12 ft), weighs 10,000 kg (22,000 lb), has a 450-kg (1000-lb) payload, and operates with a crew of two. It carries a full complement of communications and navigation equipment including two 1000-W lights on the bow, still camera with flash, two television cameras (one external and one hand-held internal), echo sounder, sonar, pinger, gyrocompass, underwater telephone, and surface radio. It has 60 heavy-duty 120-V lead-acid batteries with 385 Ahr. Propulsion is by two 5-hp reversible electric motors powering two side propellers. The manipulators include a heavy-duty claw with an 0.71-m (28-in.) grip and a 113-kg (250-lb) lift and a six-degree-of-movement general-purpose arm with an 0.18-m (7-in.) grip and a 68-kg (150-lb) lift. In addition to the PISCES class, HYCO manufactures the AQUARIUS, a smaller workboat with 370-m (1200-ft) capability; the LEO for 610-m (2000-ft) depths; and the TAURUS class, with diver lock-out and dry transfer capability and operations to 370 m (1200 ft).

Three examples of the large-sized manned submersibles are the AUGUSTE PICCARD, BEAVER MARK IV, and DEEP QUEST. These three represent developments of highly sophisticated technology for complex long-endurance missions. Each was developed for a particular market which failed to materialize for long-term support, thereby causing considerable modifications to be performed on the craft to vie for continuing support.

Horton AUGUSTE PICCARD. The AUGUSTE PICCARD was originally constructed in 1964 by Giovanola Brothers in Monthey, Switzerland to take passengers on underwater excursions in Lake Geneva. This 166,000-kg (366,000-lb), 28.8-m (93.5-ft) submersible had 20 0.15-m (6-in.) viewports on each side to accommodate 40 passengers per trip. It is designed to operate to 610-m (2000-ft) depths. It has a 6-m (19.8-ft) beam and a maximum height of 7.3 m (24 ft). Horton Maritime Explorations, Ltd. of Vancouver, Canada acquired the AUGUSTE PICCARD after the Swiss International Exposition was completed and has modified it to become a workboat. The side viewports have been sealed, but the three forward and two top viewports remain. It can now operate with a crew of eight plus two observers, with a normal life support endurance of 10 hr and an emergency maximum of 270 hr. It is powered by two lead-acid battery units wired for series or parallel connection, 240 V dc each at 1650 Ahr, rechargeable by two 90-kW 240-V diesel electric generators. Propulsion is by one 80-hp electric motor powering a single stern propeller in a maneuvering Kort nozzle rudder. An innovation, recently added, is a sail to increase speed of advance while transiting on the surface. This craft is now equipped for geophysical exploration as well as undersea inspection, with the following sensors installed: a high-resolution subbottom profiler, echo sounder, sonar, pinger, still color camera, television, videotape system, and underwater telephone. A recent, particularly interesting experiment included successfully operating a McElhanney TROV-type unmanned remotely controlled vehicle from a "garage" on the deck of the PICCARD while submerged near the sea floor. Such a combination gives this long-endurance craft a powerful capability.

IUC BEAVER MARK IV.   The BEAVER submersible, also known at one time as the ROUGHNECK, was designed and constructed by North American Rockwell, in Long Beach, California, in 1968 as a prototype work vehicle for the undersea oil fields. This 15,500-kg (34,000-lb) submersible is 6.1 by 2.9 by 3.2 m (20 by 9.5 by 10.5 ft). It has two spherical pressure hulls, one for the pilot control area and the other for a diving compartment, with connecting tunnel. It is powered by 64-V dc, 300-Ahr lead-acid batteries driving three pod-mounted 5-hp electric motors. It is capable of 2.5-knot submerged cruise speed for 12 hr or 5-knot submerged maximum speed for 5 hr. It has a maximum operating depth of 610 m (2000 ft) and maximum diver lock-out depth of 305 m (1000 ft). IUC (International Underwater Contractors, Inc.) obtained the BEAVER from Rockwell and has modified it for general use as a workboat. Included in the modifications was the installation of an 0.77-m (30-in.) diameter acrylic viewport. This large viewport plus the other six 0.12-m (5-in.) diameter viewports provide very good visibility for its wide variety of missions. The working suite of tools includes two electrohydraulic manipulators with six degrees of movement, an 0.2-m (8-in.) claw, a 1.8-m (72-in.) reach, and a 22.7-kg (50-lb) vertical lift with the arms extended. Interchangeable tools include an impact wrench, hook hand, stud gun, grapple, and centrifigal jet pump. It operates with a crew of three plus two divers with normal endurance of 12 hr and a maximum endurance of 360 workhours. The installed sensor equipment includes eight external lights, an echo sounder, sonar, pinger, television, videotape system, still color camera, and underwater telephone.

Lockheed DEEP QUEST.   The DEEP QUEST was designed and constructed by Lockheed Missiles and Space Co., Inc., Sunnyvale, California and is operated by Lockheed Ocean Laboratory, San Diego, California. This

Figure 8-26   DEEP QUEST. (Lockheed Ocean Lab.)

52,000-kg (115,000-lb) vehicle has a maximum operating depth of 2400 m (8000 ft) and can carry a payload of 3200 kg (7000 lb). Its structure is roughly 10.2 by 5.8 by 4.0 m (40 by 19 by 13 ft) (Fig. 8-26). The main pressure hull is a structure consisting of two joined 2.1-m (7-ft) diameter spheres. There is additional space aft of the control spheres for special modules to be installed, such as a diver lock-out module for two divers, a recovery systems module, or an additional pressure hull for electronic equipment. It has two 115-V dc, 230-kWh lead-acid batteries. Propulsion is provided by two 7.5-hp electric motors connected to two main aft horizontal propellers that give 2-knot submerged cruise speed for 18 hr or a maximum of 4 knots. Maneuvering is accomplished by individual control of the aft propellers, two 7.5-hp vertical thrusters and two lateral water jet thrusters, along with active surfaces of a rudder and stern plane. DEEP QUEST is normally crewed by one pilot, a navigator, and two or three observers. There is adequate life support for dives of a normal duration of 12 hr and emergency endurance of 51 hr. It carries two hydraulic manipulators each with six degrees of movement, parallel jaws with 0.2-m (8-in.) maximum opening, a 1.8-m (6-ft) reach, and a 22.8-kg (50-lb) lifting capacity. Sea floor sampling may be accomplished with a six-barrel coring unit and 1.8-m (6-ft) extendable vane shear device. Sensors include 11 external lights, a stroboscopic light, echo sounder, sonar, two pingers, cinecamera and still camera, television, videotape system, and underwater telephone. The large payload capacity and space for experimental modules provide the DEEP QUEST with an important capability that is most useful for advanced technology programs as well as for complex undersea operations.

116

Bibliography

Gray, W. E., and Fridge, D. S. (1978). How to select diving systems in offshore applications, *Ocean Industry*, Vol. 13, No. 4, April 1978.

Hales, R. (1978). *LR in Hydrospace*. Lloyd's Register Information Service, London.

Harbor Branch Foundation (1978). Harbor Branch Foundation Operational Systems. Harbor Branch Foundation, Inc., Fort Pierce, Fla.

Heckman, P. J. (1979). An untethered unmanned submersible, in *Proceedings Oceans '79*. Institute of Electrical and Electronic Engineers, San Diego.

Lloyd's Register of Shipping (1978). Register of Offshore Units, Submersibles and Diving Systems, 1977–78. Lloyd's Register of Shipping, London.

Miller, J. W. (1979). NOAA Diving Manual, Diving for Science and Technology, U.S. Government Printing Office, Washington, D.C.

Powers, W. M. (1978). Hydroproducts goes down to the sea in an RCV, *Port Talk*, November 1978.

Shilling, C. W., and Beckett, M. W. (1977). Underwater Physiology *VI*, in *Proceedings of the Sixth Symposium on Underwater Physiology*, Federation of American Societies for Experimental Biology, Bethesda, Maryland.

Talkington, H. R. (1978). Underwater work systems research and development, in *Proceedings Offshore Technology Conference 1978*. Houston.

Terry, R. D. (1966). *The Deep Submersible*. Western Periodicals Co., North Hollywood, Calif.

Vadus, J. R. (1976). International Status and Utilization of Undersea Vehicles 1976. National Oceanic and Atmospheric Administration, U.S. Department of Commerce, Rockville, Md.

9
Operational Experience

Successful utilization of undersea work systems is based on application of experience from past operations. While most undersea operations have many specific requirements, and work systems with a variety of capabilities are applied according to these specific needs, much can be learned by study of the practical experience of system operators. The analyses of past successes and failures can be the building blocks for readiness to respond to future emergencies or preparation for more routine undersea tasks. The following are descriptions of some examples of undersea operations that included particularly complicated tasks, sometimes performed under difficult circumstances.

Rescue of PISCES III

On Wednesday, August 29, 1973, the deep submersible vehicle (DSV) PISCES III sustained flooding of the after machinery compartment and sank to the ocean floor in 420 m (1375 ft) of water some 160 km (100 miles) southwest of Ireland. Trapped inside the main sphere of the vehicle were pilots Roger Mallison and Roger Chapman; about 72 hr of life support remained.

The PISCES III, owned and operated by Vickers Oceanics, Ltd., was under charter to perform tasks associated with the laying of a telephone cable from Ireland to Nova Scotia. Initial notification of the accident was received at the Naval Ocean Systems Center (NOSC), San Diego, at 0445 Wednesday, with a request for information on the status of the cable-controlled underwater recovery vehicle (CURV III). Vickers had appealed to the U.S. Navy for assistance as backup to their primary plan to raise the distressed submersible with the aid of her sister DSVs PISCES II and V, which were being airlifted to the accident scene. The Supervisor of Salvage of the U.S. Navy, with the approval of the Chief of Naval Material and the Chief of Naval Operations, accepted the action assignment and by 0900 requested that NOSC prepare the CURV III and her operating crew for earliest departure. Since lives were in jeopardy and since the life support system aboard the PISCES III was designed for just 72 hr of operation, time was of the essence in this operation.

The CURV III, shown in Figure 8-1, is the third in a series of unmanned remotely controlled vehicles developed by NOSC under the sponsorship of the Naval Sea Systems Command primarily for use in recovery of test ordnance. However, like her predecessor, the CURV I, which placed the lines to recover the hydrogen bomb off Palomares, Spain in 1966, the CURV III has been called on to respond to emergency situations.

The CURV vehicle has an open aluminum frame on which are mounted blocks of syntactic foam to provide a slight positive buoyancy. The vehicle is 1.7 m (5½ ft) wide, 2.1 m (7 ft) high, and 4.0 m (13 ft) long and weighs 2250 kg (5000 lb). The underwater vehicle is monitored and controlled via a multiconductor tether cable by operators in a control van aboard the support ship. The vehicle is equipped with electrical propulsion units, still cameras, lights, active and passive sonar, altimeter and depthometer, and two television cameras. The two television cameras, mounted on independently controlled pan-and-tilt units, have f/1.2 lenses, permitting a 45° field of view when submerged. Four 250-W headlights and one mercury vapor spotlight on each pan-and-tilt unit provide the light source for the television cameras.

A hydraulically operated manipulator functions as the tool arm to perform undersea work tasks and recovery operations. The CURV can lift up to 91 kg (200 lb) with the manipulator. For heavier objects, such as the PISCES submersible, the vehicle makes an attachment to the object with one of several special tools placed in its manipulator and then ejects the tool (to which is attached the lift line), allowing the object to be pulled to the surface with a shipboard winch. The CURV has a normal operating depth to 2100 m (7000 ft) [this depth can be increased to 3000 m (10,000 ft) in emergency situations]. Due to its electrical tether it can be operated continuously, maintaining dives of unlimited duration through changing operators in the control van on the surface.

The CURV III with associated equipment was transferred from its primary support ship to the dock at the Naval Air Station, North Island (San Diego), where all components were placed on pallets in preparation for aircraft loading by 1430 Wednesday. Two U.S. Air Force C-141 Starlifter

Figure 9-1   CURV III system mounted on the 01 deck of the John Cabot. (U.S. Navy.)

aircraft transported the vehicle, its support equipment, and crew direct from North Island to Cork, Ireland, arriving at 1930 Thursday, August 30. At Cork, the equipment was unloaded from the aircraft, transferred to a barge at the dock, and taken to the Canadian cable-laying ship John Cabot, which was lying to about 10 miles down the river, since low tide prevented her approach to the dock. By 0645 Friday, with all CURV equipment and crew embarked, the John Cabot proceeded to the accident site, arriving at about 1930 Friday.

In the meantime, the Vickers Voyager, carrying the PISCES II and V, had arrived on site, and an attempt to place a lift line was underway as the John Cabot arrived. Two lines were attached to the PISCES III by her sister DSVs, but due to their limited power a line large enough to provide a fair safety factor when lifting the great load from a pitching and heaving platform could not be placed. The seas were running high and a strong wind was blowing, making the operations most difficult.

The CURV was prepared, so as to be ready in case it would be used in another attempt to rescue the submersible. The spray from the heavy seas was great enough even on the deck of the John Cabot, 35 ft above the sea, to flood and short out the main connection of the control tether cable for the CURV to the control van (Fig. 9-1). Immediately the cable was cut and wired directly into the control console within the van. The shorted cable had disabled the gyroscopic compass within the CURV, so a small oil-filled,

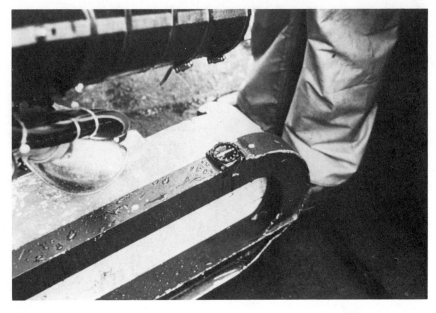

Figure 9-2   Modified diver's compass strapped to runner of CURV III. (U.S. Navy.)

pressure-compensated diver's compass was fastened to the forward starboard runner within the view of the starboard television camera (Fig. 9-2).

A recovery attachment device, a large toggle bolt manufactured by
Vickers, was given to the U.S. Navy crew for use on the CURV. Since the after
hatch of the PISCES III was open, the easiest place to make an attachment for
lifting the submersible was through this hatch. Also, most of the submersible
was covered by a fiberglass fairing, which could not sustain the loads
needed for lifting. Since the vehicle had sunk when the after machinery
compartment flooded, it was sitting tail down with the hatch opening in a
perpendicular plane. It was feared that if the toggle bolt was placed horizontally into the hatch opening the retainer bars might not properly engage
without a spring retriever, so the device was modified by welding to it a
standoff (a wrench), tied with bungee cord as springs, shown in Figure 9-3.
The whole modified toggle bolt was then welded to a spare CURV tool
holder, which was then inserted into the hydraulically activated manipulator. A 20-cm (8-in.) (circumference), double-braided nylon line was
attached to the toggle bolt, then taped (with low strength masking tape) to
the CURV frame, and taped at intervals all along the tether cable (Fig. 9-4).

At 0900 Saturday, September 1, a Vickers representative arrived
aboard the John Cabot and requested that the CURV be sent to the PISCES III to
attempt to attach the heavy lift line. At 0942, the CURV was over the side

Figure 9-3   Specially fabricated toggle attachment tool mounted in CURV III tool arm. (U.S. Navy.)

Figure 9-4   Bow of the John Cabot showing CURV III tether and nylon recovery rope. (U.S. Navy.)

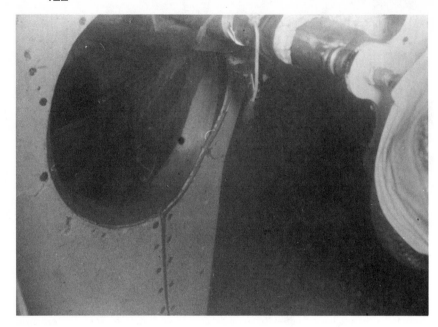

Figure 9-5   CURV III inserting toggle attachment tool into hatch of PISCES III. (U.S. Navy.)

ready to dive. At 1030, it arrived on the bottom at a 460-m (1500-ft) depth and commenced a 360° sonar scan. A large sonar target was detected at 220 m (240 yd). The bottom current was estimated at about 0.5 knot. The sonar target was closed, classified as PISCES III, and the toggle bolt placed by 1040 (see Fig. 9-5). It was ascertained that the toggle bolt was secure by observing it via the television camera.

Then a strain was put on the lift line by the John Cabot, the tool holder was ejected from the CURV manipulator, the masking tape ties broke as the lift cable separated from the CURV tether, and the lift of the PISCES III was begun. By 1300, the submersible had been raised to the surface (Fig. 9-6), and an additional line was being attached by swimmers so that it could be held horizontally for the egress of the personnel. By 1320, the men had climbed out and were transferred, in good condition, via rubber boat to the Vickers Voyager. Although 70 hr had passed since the start of the initial dive and the life support system was designed for 72-hr duration, it was estimated that the two men could have safely remained within the submersible for an additional 12–15 hr. Both men in the PISCES III were experienced in diving as well as submersible piloting, and they exercised considerable restraint during their wait for rescue by relaxation, sleeping, and taking other measures to reduce their metabolic rate, thereby conserving the oxygen supply and the carbon dioxide absorbant.

Figure 9-6 PISCES III lifted to surface by nylon rope. (U.S. Navy.)

The water was pumped out of the after machinery compartment, and the PISCES III was then returned to the Vickers Voyager, thus completing not only the rescue of the two pilots but also the salvage of their submersible. The John Cabot returned to Cork where the CURV system was off-loaded, transferred to the airfield and the two C-141 aircraft, and returned to the NOSC San Diego home base.

The success of this emergency operation was due to the tremendous cooperation extended by a multinational task force including the men and equipment of the British Vickers Voyager and PISCES II and V, the Canadian cable-laying ship John Cabot, the Irish shore support, and the U.S. Navy CURV III system along with its U.S. Air Force air transportation.

Repairs to an Undersea Tower

During its installation onto the sea floor at a depth of about 760 m (2500 ft), a 68-metric-ton (75-ton) tower was dropped, and the impact damaged part of the substructure. This tower was about 31 m (100 ft) high and consisted of a steel frame with floats at the top and anchors at the bottom of the legs. A large 7.5-cm- (3-in.-) diameter electrical cable connected the tower to a shore installation. To properly complete the installation, the tower had to be

124

recovered, repaired, reinstalled, and inspected. This required a sequence of undersea tasks that exercised a wide variety of undersea sensors and tools.

This example again involves use of the cable-controlled unmanned vehicle CURV III. The CURV III, with its crew, was transported to the nearest seaport and there installed on a support ship. The initial task was to locate and inspect the tower, ascertain its condition, determine the sequence of operations to effect recovery, and define the tools required. Since no personnel were in danger, and, therefore, no rescue required, the operation was planned to take advantage of best sea surface conditions. The initial dive utilized the high-resolution sonar to acquire the tower, which provided a very large sonar return. The inspection was documented by videotapes of the images from the two television cameras plus color slides from the 35-mm still camera. The inspection disclosed that the lifting eye at the top of the tower was fouled with a tangle of the broken handling line; the rest of the tower was intact enough to be recovered once the shore-connected instrumentation cable was disconnected.

The second task consisted of carrying a cable clamp, attached by a line to a surface buoy, down to the undersea cable at a point about 15 m (50 ft) away from the tower and attaching it firmly (Fig. 9-7). Then a cable-cutting device consisting of four pyronol torches (Fig. 9-8) was attached to the cable between the clamp and the tower. Activation of the torches cut the cable

Figure 9-7   Mechanical cable clamp. (U.S. Navy.)

Figure 9-8   Pyronol cutters being placed on cable. (U.S. Navy.)

cleanly, and the buoyed cable clamp provided a means to recover the end of the cable for later connection during the reinstallation process.

A dive was made to clear the entangled lifting eye by use of cutters for both steel cable and nylon lines. A 76-m (250-ft) length of large-diameter nylon line was connected to a large shackle at one end and to a large snap hook at the other. Since the tower was much too heavy for the CURV III to lift, a large lift ship was positioned nearby and its lifting bail lowered to the sea floor, about 46 m (150 ft) from the tower. The nylon line was coiled into a container on board the CURV III vehicle and the shackle and snap hook placed on the vehicle so the manipulators could make the connections. This whole set of rigging was transported down to the top of the tower where the shackle, which had a remotely releasable spring-loaded pin, was inserted into the lifting eye and the pin actuated to effect closure (see Fig. 9-9). Next the CURV III swam from the tower to the bail of the lift ship, deploying the nylon line along the way, and attached the snap hook (Fig. 9-10) to the bail. The tower, now being free of the cable, was lifted to the surface and returned to shore for repairs.

Upon completion of repairs, the tower was returned to the site. The undersea cable was recovered, by use of the buoyed line, and connected to the tower. The tower was then reinstalled without mishap. The final inspection of the installation by the CURV III using videotape and 35-mm cameras confirmed a proper installation.

Figure 9-9 Remotely operated shackle placed in tower lifting eye. (U.S. Navy.)

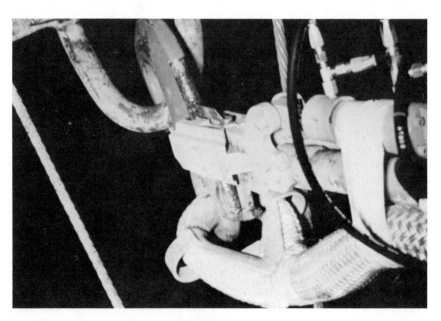

Figure 9-10 Attaching hook to lifting bale. (U.S. Navy.)

This operation exercised a large number of sensors and tools and required the development of a couple of specialized attachment devices that have since proved useful elsewhere. Many individual dives were required, with precise vehicle maneuvering by experienced operators the key to the successful placement of the several devices. This program demonstrated the need for a balanced set of sensors, tools, transport vehicle, and experienced operators for the successful completion of a complex operation.

Installation of the Base Section of the Cognac Platform

The Hydro Products RCV 225* (Fig. 9-11), operated by the Taylor Diving Company of Belle Chasse, Louisiana, performed a primary role in the initial phases of installation of the Shell Oil Company's Cognac platform in water over 310 m (1000 ft) deep. The basic task for the phase was to transport to

*RCV is a registered trademark of Hydro Products, inc.

Figure 9-11 Hydro Products RCV 225 in its garage being lowered into the sea. (Hydro Products, Inc.)

Figure 9-12   RCV 225 conducting inspection. (Hydro Products, Inc.)

the site, lower, and fasten into place on the sea floor the jacket base section (JBS). The JBS itself is a major structure of more than 31 m (100 ft) on a side, made up of a complex of steel members. The remotely controlled vehicle RCV 225, described in Chapter 8, and its crew were utilized to perform the following operations:

1. The designated operators frequently visited the JBS construction site to become completely familiar with the mammoth structure. This included monitoring of the final inspection and checkout prior to load out.
2. The first task was performance of a complete visual bottom survey of the intended site prior to commencement of operations.
3. After the JBS was launched and floating above the intended site, the RCV conducted a visual inspection of all parts of the structure that were underwater (Fig. 9-12), to verify that no damage was incurred during launching. Although this operation was only to depths of 37 m (120 ft), it saved considerable costs over use of divers, and the safety engineers could directly observe the results.
4. As the JBS was lowered to the sea floor, the RCV followed it to check depth, attitude, and orientation and to observe bottom impact and penetration.

5. The RCV was then used to monitor the lowering and "stabbing" of the piles that fastened the JBS firmly to the sea floor.
6. During all deep-diving operations, an RCV accompanied the divers. As the diving bell was lowered to the vicinity of the worksite, the RCV launcher was lowered nearby. The RCV was deployed to the worksite for a preoperational check of conditions. If all were well, the RCV would then be turned to point toward the diving bell to provide the diver with a beacon (a visual target) toward which to swim. This provided the secondary benefit of allowing the surface support personnel to observe the diver. The RCV was then used as a light source to assist the diver in his work tasks and as a continuing safety monitor system. On several occasions, the RCV performed simple tasks to support the divers, such as untangling lines and freeing fouled hoses.
7. The final task on the Cognac JBS was the observation and testing of the setup of the grouting as it was placed in the structural sleeves. The RCV observed the flow, checked for spillage, and entered the sleeve to check for hardness.

The RCV 225 and other small unmanned remotely controlled vehicles have proven to be cost-effective systems for supporting undersea installations such as the Cognac and other platforms in deep water. Diving contractors have found them to be most useful, that is, complementary to their divers and not as competitive with regard to work as first feared.

Recovery of an Aircraft Flight Recorder

A complex operation, that becomes very high priority, is the recovery of the flight recorder from downed aircraft. When the aircraft is down in the sea, often with extensive damage, the task becomes even more difficult. Several such operations have been accomplished under a wide variety of environmental conditions. Since this will remain a high-priority task and will require repetition, under varying conditions in the future, a discussion of the individual portions of the operation may be of assistance to a prospective undersea work system designer or operator. The following is a description of the steps and tools required in a generic scenario for recovery of a flight recorder from an aircraft downed in the sea.

Initially, the aircraft must be located, its position marked, and its condition ascertained. This portion of the task is often the most difficult and time-consuming, but since this discussion is to cover the undersea work required to remove the flight recorder, we start with the assumption of completion of the location task and the marking of the specific portion of the wreckage that contains the flight recorder. Detail aircraft design information is required to specify the exact spot to commence cutting into the structure. The following steps are one sequence of operations successfully used in the past:

1. Drill a small pilot hole through the aircraft skin.
2. Enlarge the hole with a larger drill.
3. Insert a hydraulic spreader into the enlarged hole, and rip the skin horizontally and vertically until structural members are encountered.
4. Insert either a reciprocating saw or a hydraulic jack, and cut or spread the structure to provide a large enough hole to provide access to the flight recorder.
5. Attach a line to the recorder, and tie it off to the work system.
6. Remove the mounting bolts, and release the recorder package.
7. Return the recorder to the surface either by transporting by the vehicle or diver or by use of an inflatable buoyancy bag.

This sequence of tasks has been carried out by divers and by manipulative tools from both submersibles and unmanned vehicles. The order and size of tools utilized will vary with availability and the condition of the wreckage. Sometimes it may even be easier to salvage the remaining aircraft hull around the recorder. The type of transporter, that is, diver versus vehicle, will primarily depend on the depth of the operation. It is most important to obtain a complete description of the wreckage and then to carefully define, step by step, the expected sequence of tasks and the tools and sensors to observe the tools prior to commencing the operation.

Undersea Systems Safety

Undersea operations involving manned systems require particular emphasis on safety. Several good documents have been prepared to assist the potential designer and operator of submersibles. The Marine Technology Society (MTS) has taken the lead in defining guidelines for safer systems and operations. Listed in the bibliography of this chapter are three invaluable books produced by the Undersea Vehicle Committee of the MTS under the able direction of Mr. John Pritzlaff. The following are some introductory considerations regarding advance planning and devices for "self-help" as applied to submersibles.

A review of the operations for the rescue of the submersibles JOHNSON-SEALINK, PISCES III, and PC-9 indicated several features of submersible system design that greatly impacted their safe recovery. To the extent that these items were already incorporated in the individual submersible system (which here included the surface support equipment), a simpler, more expedient rescue was performed. In addition to items immediately available to the submersible, either as part of the craft or as part of the system on the surface tending vessel, two items of information proved to be of special importance: (1) the detailed description of the distressed craft and (2) the knowledge of the characteristics and location of equipment that could be called upon for emergency assistance.

Particular items are recommended for use with submersibles, and other high-value targets, that will significantly expedite emergency search and recovery operations should the vehicles become lost. These are described in the following paragraphs:

1. *Position indicator.* An acoustic beacon operating on a standard distress frequency placed on a manned target would automatically actuate whenever a critical depth was exceeded. To respond with rapid large-area search afforded by aircraft deployed and monitored sonobuoy sensors, it is recommended that the beacon operate on multifrequencies: 4 kHz for sonobuoy detection and 9 and 37 kHz for final approach.

2. *External standard lift points.* Clearly marked standardized lift points installed on all high-value targets would allow a distressed vehicle to be easily lifted to safety. An example of one possible configuration is shown in Fig. 9-13. Here, two 20-cm- (8-in.-) diameter rings are placed 90° apart and fastened securely to strong points on the vehicle structure. Lift points should be strong enough to allow for total lift of the vehicle. Care must be taken to ensure that vehicle lift points are located to allow easy accessibility during rescue, but they should not protrude to the point that they would snag other objects during normal operations.

3. *Minimum life support.* Adequate life support on board a stricken vessel is imperative to ensure the safety of the crew until emergency rescue

Figure 9-13   Example of an external lifting ring for submersible safety. (U.S. Navy.)

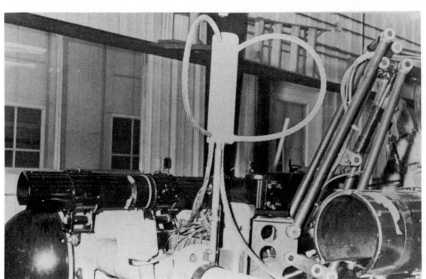

can be made. Further, minimum life support should be established for each operating submersible, and a dive should not take place if an inventory check shows the submersible to be deficient. Minimum life support items such as oxygen, air purifiers, heat, and necessary power support must be carefully established for each vehicle and a rigid predive checkoff instigated. A minimum life support duration of between 24 and 72 hr, dependent on local conditions of support, should be provided.

4. *Acoustic communications.* A standard 8-11-kHz underwater telephone installed on all submersibles would allow for verbal communications between rescuers and rescuees.

5. *Minimum operator qualification.* Proficiency training should be required for all submersible pilots—particularly emergency safety and survival procedures—and a program of periodic proficiency checks would give operators the confidence and knowledge needed in case of an emergency.

6. *File dive plan with a potential rescue unit.* The provision that all submersible operators be required to file a dive plan prior to all undersea operations would enable the U.S. Coast Guard, U.S. Navy, or other rescue unit to monitor all operations and devise realistic emergency contingency plans.

7. *Passenger predive briefing.* A passenger on board a submersible should be thoroughly briefed on emergency and survival procedures prior to a dive in case the pilot, however well trained and qualified, should suffer injury or be incapacitated during a dive. Also, an emergency bill should be plainly posted inside the submersible to minimize reaction time.

8. *Color.* A target colored either white or yellow would greatly assist location of the vehicle during rescue. As a minimum, the target should be painted with easily identifiable checkerboard or other patterns in white or yellow. These colors are more readily seen than others under water. As a further aid, the use of reflecting materials is also recommended.

9. *Marker buoy.* A small automatically or crew-operated marker buoy installed on all submersibles could be used to mark the location of the stricken vessel as well as provide a light line to the surface. This line could then act as a guide line for lowering a heavier lifting line to the submersible. As an example of such a buoy is shown in Figure 9-14.

10. *Support ship recovery capability.* Since the submersible support ship immediately becomes the primary recovery vessel when a submersible accident occurs and maintains its new status until outside assistance arrives, it must be prepared and equipped to assume this critically important role. As a minimum the support ship should have a winch and line on board that could be used to haul the stricken submersible from its operating depth to the surface, and preferably it should be strong enough to lift the vehicle onto the deck.

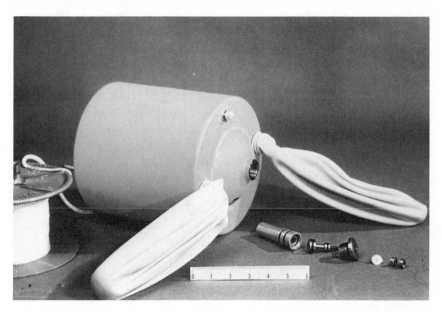

Figure 9-14   One type of releasable marker buoy for submersible safety. (U.S. Navy.)

Figure 9-15   ELECTRIC SNOOPY outfitted with snap hook attachment tool and a buoyant reel for marking a distressed submersible. (U.S. Navy.)

11. *Emergency plan.* A hazards analysis and compatible emergency plan should be developed that would anticipate each potential accident or dangerous condition. A counterplan should be ready which would include details of any special equipment needed on board both the submersible and the support ship to properly react to the emergency and would describe the action required by the crews of both craft. These should be prepared for each particular task and take into account the operating environment the submersible may encounter during a given deployment.

12. *Description of submersibles.* A complete and up-to-date description of each submersible vehicle that includes drawings which depict hard points, a description of rescue/salvage scenarios, and any other information pertinent to rescue/salvage operations would significantly aid the rescue team and increase the assurance of a safe rescue.

13. *Location of contingency assistance.* The location and characteristics of the nearest undersea vehicle with a capability to render emergency assistance should be ascertained. The operators of the vehicle (manned or unmanned) should be contacted and notified of the intended operation and a contingency plan prepared for emergency response. Figure 9-15 shows the ELECTRIC SNOOPY with an example of an emergency recovery suite aboard, including a buoyant reel with 460 m (1500 ft) of KEVLAR line and a simple attachment hook.

Bibliography

Chew, J. I., and Johnston, J. R. (1979). The Use of Unmanned Remote Controlled Vehicles for Offshore Inspection and Work Tasks. SPE 7769, presented at the Society of Petroleum Engineers Conference, 25–29 March 1979. Society of Petroleum Engineers, Dallas.

Geyer, R. A. (1977). *Submersibles and Their Use in Oceanography and Ocean Engineering.* Elsevier, Amsterdam.

Johnston, J. R. (1979). Remote Controlled Vehicle Update. Presented at the International Diving Symposium 1979. Hydro Products, Inc., San Diego.

Talkington, H. R. (1974). U.S. Navy participation in the rescue of the PISCES III, *Marine Technology Society Journal,* Vol. 8, No. 1, January 1974.

Talkington, H. R. (1975). Self-help rescue capability for submersibles, *Marine Technology Society Journal,* Vol. 9, No. 4, April–May 1975.

Undersea Vehicle Committee (1968). Safety and Operational Guidelines for Undersea Vehicles, Book I. Marine Technology Society, Washington, D.C.

Undersea Vehicle Committee (1974). Safety and Operational Guidelines for Undersea Vehicles, Book II. Marine Technology Society, Washington, D.C.

Undersea Vehicle Committee (1979). International Safety Standard Guidelines for the Operation of Undersea Vehicles. Marine Technology Society, Washington, D.C.

10
System Synthesis

Synthesis is defined in the *American Heritage Dictionary* as "the combining of separate elements or substances to form a coherent whole." The many elements, procedures, and philosophy of design of undersea work systems have been discussed in the preceding chapters. A recurring theme has been careful planning and definition of requirements such that a "coherent whole" may result from system development efforts. Many of the vehicles and devices described in Chapter 8 could be utilized as examples of the final achievement of system synthesis, since their operations provide a measure of performance against their original expectations. However, for this chapter, an advanced system has been selected for analysis—an undersea system more complex and difficult to construct than any previously attempted. This proposed system is truly the ultimate challenge in the future field of ocean engineering. The undersea work systems required to implement this concept will stress the imagination and ingenuity of engineers and scientists for some time to come. The DUMAND project is in the earliest definition phase with only broad concepts currently being considered. Whether this particular project proceeds in the current projected configuration or not, it still serves as a marvelous example of undersea work systems "synthesis."

Description of the System

DUMAND, the acronym for deep underwater muon and neutrino detection, is a project started by a group of U.S. physicists to produce a detector large enough to detect a significant rate of very high-energy neutrinos. This will permit the study of elementary particle interactions in cosmic rays at energies beyond those available from contemplated future particle accelerators. It may also allow the observation of extraterrestrial and possibly extragalactic sources of neutrinos.

For elementary particle research the energies sought here—10^{14} eV (100,000 billion electron volts) and above—are necessary to probe the structure of particles on the minutest possible scale and to test our presently emerging picture of the fundamental forces of nature. A very large detector is also necessary to make high-energy neutrino astronomy a reality, because of the background of terrestrial neutrinos made by cosmic-ray protons in the earth's atmosphere. At very high energies the flux from beyond the earth will surely dominate. If the sources that we believe exist do produce an observable flux of extraterrestrial neutrinos, we shall have begun a new field of science and opened a new window upon the universe.

The techniques available for detecting high-energy neutrino collisions in the ocean utilize either the light flash that the particles produce (Cerenkov radiation) or the acoustic pulse they emit (by instantaneously heating a tiny volume of water). The ocean is simultaneously our target, detection medium, and shield from external disturbances. One detector configuration, at 5100 m (3000 fathoms) depth, will consist of a volumetric array of 22,680 sensors evenly placed on a three-dimensional grid at spacings of about 40 m (130 ft). It is presently envisioned as a group of vertical strings of sensors, anchored to the bottom and kept in near-vertical orientation by high tension provided by excess buoyancy at the top of each string. Initially, primary detection will be concentrated on the optical signals, and the sensors described in the "standard" array will be optimized for the optical phenomena.

The current standard detector array, defined at the 1978 DUMAND Summer Workshop, is configured as a squat hexagon of 800 m (2600 ft) on a side and 673 m (2200 ft) high (see Fig. 10-1). Within this hexagon, which encloses 1.29×10^9 m³ of water, are 22,680 optical sensors. Eighteen sensors are placed on each vertical string at 36.6-m (120-ft) spacing. Twenty-one strings of sensors are tied to baselines at 40-m (130-ft) spacings to create a plane of 378 sensors. Twenty planes of sensors are placed parallel with each other at 40-m (130-ft) spacings along each of three legs. The three legs are placed in a "Y" configuration with one end of each touching and connected to a master computer/processing station, each leg at a 120° angle with the others. As shown in Figure 10-2, this forms a hexagon with 800-m (2600-ft) sides. Undersea cabling will connect the sea

MAUI SHORE STATION

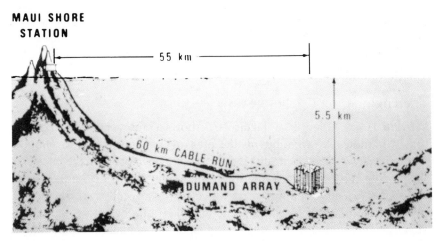

Figure 10-1   1978 model of the DUMAND array. (DUMAND Project.)

floor master computer/processing station to a nearby shore station where control, monitoring, recording, and analysis will take place.

Uses for the System

The DUMAND system will allow high-energy physicists to conduct basic investigations into the very nature of the universe: (1) using the detector array as a microscope to determine particle physics interactions associated

Figure 10-2   Plane view of the 1978 DUMAND array. (DUMAND Project.)

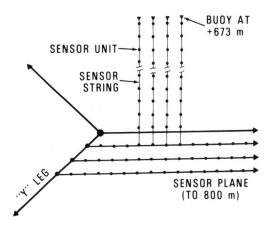

with the passage of neutrinos and (2) using the detector array as a telescope to investigate the origins of extraterrestrial neutrinos. Each of the objectives involves energies in orders of magnitude beyond those now possible or even contemplated with nuclear particle accelerators. For those with an interest in additional uses of the DUMAND system, the documents listed in the bibliography of this chapter are recommended.

The Engineering Challenge

Individual Parts.   Sensors.   Figure 10-3 shows a cross section of an optical sensor module. As the blue-hued Cerenkov radiation from a muon or hadronic shower passes through the transparent envelope into the interior of the module, it is absorbed by the wavelength shifter fluid and then reemitted and shifted to a more yellow color. This yellow light is collected and focused into a group of detectors. The photomultiplier tube detectors register the signal and pass it to the first stage of signal processing electronics built into every sensor module. The transparent materials, the photomultiplier tubes, and the electronics (which are to be pressure tolerant) all present major engineering problems for operational conditions of 6000-m (18,000-ft) depth, presence of fouling organisms, 10-year minimum life, and very high reliability.

Figure 10-3   Optical sensor module. (DUMAND Project.)

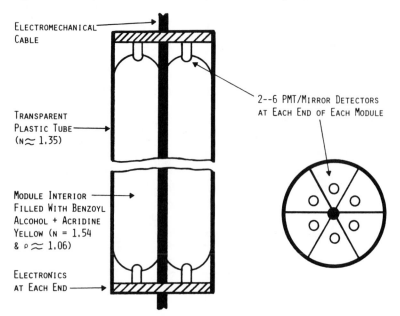

ELECTROMECHANICAL CABLE

2--6 PMT/MIRROR DETECTORS AT EACH END OF EACH MODULE

TRANSPARENT PLASTIC TUBE ($n \approx 1.35$)

MODULE INTERIOR FILLED WITH BENZOYL ALCOHOL + ACRIDINE YELLOW ($n = 1.54$ & $\rho \approx 1.06$)

ELECTRONICS AT EACH END

Strings. The 673-m (2200-ft) high strings each include 18 optical sensor modules at 36.6-m (120-ft) spacings. The sensors are connected by a composite strength and signal cable. Each string has its own tensioning/positioning buoy located immediately above the highest sensor module. The function of the buoy is to hold the string in a near-vertical position and to keep it from entangling with adjacent sensor strings. The string has an electrical connection point at its base to connect it to a distribution line along the base of the plane and to anchor it to resist the tension caused by the buoy. The materials for long-term buoyancy, the cabling at minimum cost and weight, and the base anchor and electrical and mechanical tiedown/connection require application of undersea engineering.

Sensor Planes. Twenty-one strings at 40-m (130-ft) spacing constitute a 800-m- (2600-ft-) long by 673-m- (2200-ft-) high sensor plane. A distribution line, with composite strength and signal transmission cable characteristics, connects junction positions at each 40 m (130 ft), where both the electrical and mechanical connections to the strings occur. The cable, electrical connection points, and means of anchoring are each expected to be fairly routine engineering designs.

Legs. Extending out 800 m (2600 ft) from the central core are the three basic legs of the system. It is envisioned that these three legs will be built as fixed stiff structures and will each contain the automatic interconnection points for the distribution lines for the 20 planes. Since it is envisioned that the connection of the planes to the legs will be made in situ, both the mechanical and electrical connections must be capable of being remotely accomplished in a pressurized wet environment. Again, the cable materials and the mechanical and electrical connections require advanced engineering design, and the members for the 800-m- (2600-ft-) long legs will require some ingenious design to minimize cost and weight for such long stiff structures.

Signal Processing. The individual optical signals arriving at each of the 12 photomultiplier tubes in each optical sensor must be detected and correlated with the signals received by the other photomultipliers and sensor modules. To determine direction and velocity of particle tracks, signals detected by large numbers of modules from various strings must be correlated with a precise time base. In addition, a continuous updating of the sensor module's relative location must be accomplished, most likely using an acoustic beacon/receiver tracking system. These requirements collectively necessitate that an extremely large amount of data be handled by the electronic and communication system. A very thorough trade-off study must be made as to distributed processing at the string or even module level versus sizes and types of cabling back to the central computer/processing station connected at the center of the array.

Main Cable.   The central computer/processor at the center of the array will be connected to a nearby shore station to provide the power source and control for the undersea system. The computer/processor equipment will be installed in a water-resistant container and, if possible, be oil-filled and pressure-compensated and then placed on the sea floor as the interface between the shore cable and the array. The design of the computing equipment for long-term (10-year) pressure-tolerant operation and the materials for the main cable are the engineering tasks for this portion of the system.

Summary.   The individual parts of the system, the deep-water location, the organic fouling environment, the undersea currents and turbidity, the long-term untended nature of the system, the criticality of weight and volume on deployment techniques, and the costs that are multipled by the extreme

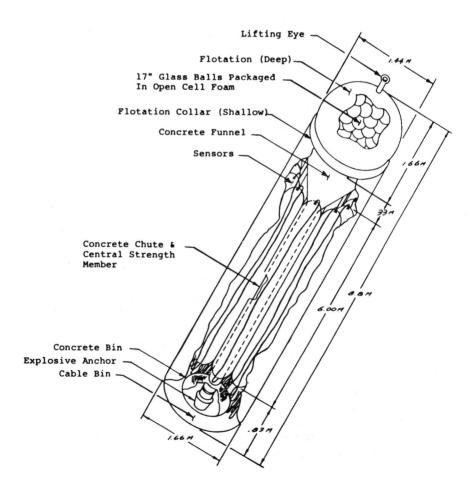

Figure 10-4   Sensor-string deployment canister. (DUMAND Project.)

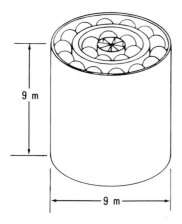

9 m

9 m

Figure 10-5   Sensor-plane deployment module. (DUMAND Project.)

numbers of components required (e.g., 22,680 sensor modules) all demand the utmost in careful precise engineering.

Deployment.   Utilizing existing ocean engineering technology and such unique assets as remotely controlled undersea vehicles and offshore oil exploration drill ships, several deployment concepts have been developed and appear feasible. The dominant constraint faced (and accepted) was the need to deploy and implant the DUMAND optical array in large modules. This means that each transported and deployed unit must represent a relatively large fraction of the total array volume. The sensor plane was chosen as the monolithic deployed unit, with containerized vertical sensor strings as subunits. This approach was chosen based on need to reduce the cost, time, and risk for array deployment.

The full impact of the size of the components of the DUMAND array may best be appreciated by its relationship to other more usual physical objects. A sensor plane 800 m (2600 ft) long is 2⅓ times the length of the nuclear-powered aircraft carrier USS Enterprise or eight football fields. Its height, 673 m (2000 ft), is twice the length of that carrier or nearly twice the height of the Empire State Building in New York City. The physical structure of the array has an in-air weight of 14,000 metric tons (15,400 tons), but can be constructed with components to have the same overall specific gravity of seawater to ease the undersea lowering and placing loads. Once the realization of size is understood, the construction and deployment challenge is fully appreciated.

As noted, the modular approach at the string and plane level was selected for deployment scheme trade-offs. Each vertical string is packaged into a cylindrical canister (Fig. 10-4) which is approximately 1.66 m (5.4 ft) wide and 8.8 m (29 ft) long. Then 21 of these canisters are packed into a larger canister that becomes the plane deployment module (Fig. 10-5). It is envisioned that the assembly of the deployment modules will be accomplished at a shore installation near the sea floor site and will be loaded aboard semisubmerged barges for transport to the sea site. At the site, the modules will be floated off the barges and rigged for lowering. The use of semisubmerged craft negates the need for large cranes to lift the modules at sea. The following are six concepts for deploying the modules to the sea floor.

Concept 1. This approach assembles sections of the array into relatively rigid and rugged structural templates, which are towed to the site and lowered to the sea floor on a drill string from a ship, such as the Glomar Challenger. It is sketched in Figure 10-6. The general approach is summarized as follows:

Phase 1   Shore assembly and launch.
Phase 2   Tow to site utilizing large surface floats or pontoons lashed to the sides of the template.
Phase 3   Submerge the template to about an 250-m (800-ft) depth (by releasing line from the floats) and then position it under the drill ship. Once attachment to the drill string has been made, lower the template to the sea floor. The operation is repeated (108 cycles) until all templates have been emplanted.

Concept 2. This approach allows a deployment module to drop to the sea floor along a restraining cable, which is supported by a small stable surface platform. The lower end of the cable supports, powers, and controls a small tethered vehicle which has sufficient in-water weight to keep the line nearly plumb in any expected current. The tethered vehicle is equipped with thrusters for X-Y propulsion, lights, television, high-resolution sonar, and a two-handed manipulator system. It also has a hook to support moderately heavy lifting and positioning operations.

After impact, the tethered vehicle (Fig. 10-7) picks up the deployment module, which has a relatively low in-water weight. It carries the module along the sensor plane, successively dropping each sensor-string canister at its planned position. Final operations include electrical attachment of the sensor plane to the junction box on the Y leg, anchoring each sensor string to the sea floor (probably with a harpoon anchor), and release of the buoyancy floats for each sensor string.

Concept 3. The 21 canisters of each sensor plane are laid out near the ocean surface, supported by a row of buoyancy floats. They are joined by their interconnection cables and (perhaps) by ancillary ropes. Two workboats, each supporting a tethered vehicle with heavy-duty propulsion capability, form attachments to the ends of the sensor plane (Fig. 10-8). The

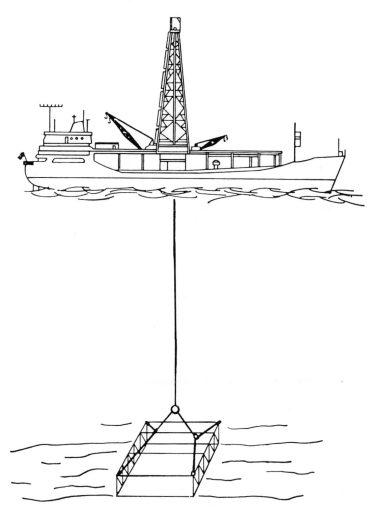

Figure 10-6   Concept 1: template deployment. (DUMAND Project.)

surface floats are cut, and the module begins to sink under lifting and positioning control from the tethered vehicle. They are guided to the sea floor
position planned for the sensor plane. At this point, one of the tethered
vehicles continues with the same electrical connection, anchoring, and
buoy-release tasks already described for concept 2.

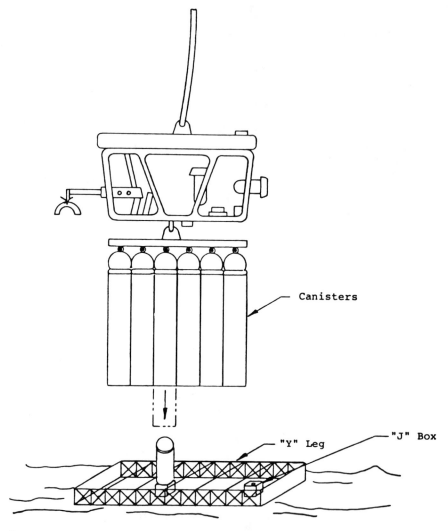

Figure 10-7   Concept 2: vehicle placement of sensor canisters. (DUMAND Project.)

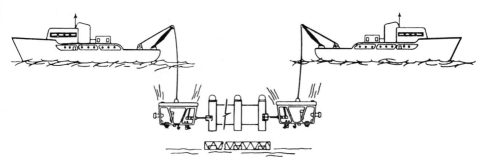

Figure 10-8   Concept 3: deployment with two workboats and two vehicles. (DUMAND Project.)

Concept 4.   In this approach, each of DUMAND's 1261 sensor strings is deployed from a small support ship (Fig. 10-9). As in all other deployment concepts, the strings are canisterized. The ship places a canister in the water so that it hangs vertically from a surface float and has a heavy "smart" clump hanging below it. This complex is towed to a point roughly over the desired emplantment point, as the ship navigates with respect to a set of (at least) three acoustic transponders previously placed on the sea floor around the perimeter of the array site. When the desired position is reached, the float line is cut, and the canister begins to fall in the general direction of its assigned $X_0 - Y_0$ position on the sea floor.

The package hanging below contains a guidance system that responds to a previously laid, bottom acoustic navigation system and guides the free-falling module to its intended location on the sea floor. After many canisters have been dropped, a surface-tethered undersea vehicle is used to connect each string either to an adjacent string or to a plane cable. At the same time, the guidance/control units will be removed from the anchor and allowed to float buoyantly to the surface for recovery and reuse.

Concept 5.   This approach combines a drill ship with a surface-supported "tugger" tethered vehicle. The 21 sensor-string canisters of a full sensor plane are towed to the site aboard a submerged transporter barge. They are then pulled from that platform so that they hang from surface floats in a roughly linear array. Support launches would pull on the end floats to keep the system under tension. The drill string is (loosely) attached to the canister at one end of the sensor plane and the workboat to the canister at the other end. All support craft clear the scene, and the system is ready for lowering. As the drill string begins its descent, the supporting floats are sequentially cut free.

The workboat maintains a position to hold a slight tension on the connecting cables to allow proper spacing during the descent to the sea

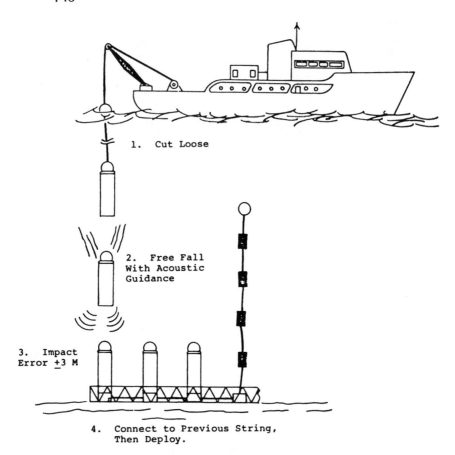

1. Cut Loose

2. Free Fall
    With Acoustic
    Guidance

3. Impact
    Error +3 M

4. Connect to Previous String,
    Then Deploy.

Figure 10-9   Concept 4: sensor-string canisters free-fall to the sea floor. (DUMAND Project.)

floor. At the end of the plane, a tugger vehicle (thruster), operating on an umbilical from the workboat, continues to apply tension to the sensor plane throughout descent (Fig. 10-10). The drill string with the first canister reaches the bottom, very close to the Y cable leg to establish a positioning reference. The second and sequential canisters are then lowered to the sea floor as the tugger vehicle maintains control of sensor-plane azimuth for accurate placement of individual sensor canisters.

When the last canister is on the bottom, the tugger vehicle can be recovered by the workboat. The drill string's powered clump then makes the electrical connection to the Y cable and inspects the results of the deployment. Prior to deployment of the sensor-string floats, the drill ship positions itself above each canister, and concrete is pumped down the drill string to

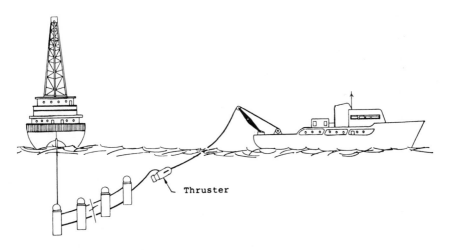

Figure 10-10 Concept 5: deployment by drill ship and surface-supported tugger vehicle. (DUMAND Project.)

provide an anchor. When the concrete anchors are in place, the sensor floats can be deployed.

Concept 6. Each sensor string is packaged into a cylindrical canister, and 21 string canisters are packed into a larger canister that becomes a deployment module. This module is attached to the drill stem of a deep-sea drilling ship along with a tethered unmanned vehicle (Fig. 10-11) and is deployed as discussed in the following steps:

    1. Near the sea floor, guided by the vehicle's navigation system, the drill stem is maneuvered to the intersection of the sensor plane with its Y cable. The sensor-plane cable is connected to the Y cable. The vehicle's manipulators should readily perform this task, using simple rotary "wet" connectors of either the coaxial or inductive coupler type.

    2. By using navigational guidance from the vehicle, the drill stem is successively placed over each of the preplanned sensor-string sites. [Error in the X-Y plane should be less than ± 2 m (6 ft).] Each sensor string is placed by releasing its canister from the main module and allowing it to free-fall 12–15 m (40–50 ft) to the sea floor. The canister's low in-water weight should ensure a soft landing. The vehicle can be used here to pull a lanyard to release the canister. This operation continues with 40-m (130-ft) spacing along the sensor plane until all 21 canisters have been dropped.

    3. The vehicle and drill stem move back along the sensor plane. At each of the canisters, the vehicle actuates a device which drives a harpoon anchor into the sea floor. The required holding power should not be more than about 1 metric ton.

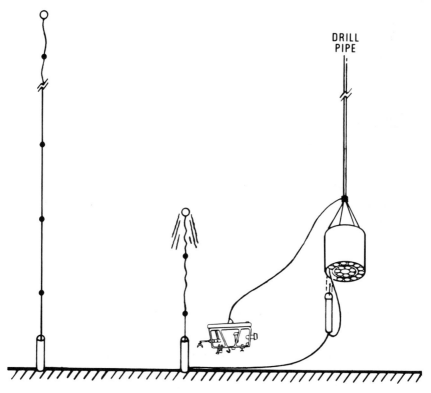

Figure 10-11   Concept 6: deployment by drill ship and tethered unmanned vehicle. (DUMAND Project.)

4. The vehicle returns to each sensor string canister and pulls a lanyard to open a hatch and release the tensioning buoy. The sensor-string cable and sensor units are lifted to their 673-m (2200-ft) design height.

5. The drill pipe is lifted—section by section—and the relatively light housing for the sensor-plane module is refitted with suspension floats so that it can be transported back to shore for reloading.

In each deployment concept a transport vessel is required to move the modules from the shore assembly base to the sea installation site. Two types of transport vessels are considered: a pontoon catamaran that would submerge the canisters about 90% to minimize sail area exposure and a submergible barge that would allow the canisters to be totally submerged.

Undersea Vehicle   Several of the deployment concepts also require the use of a powered clump or surface-tethered, remotely operated undersea vehicle to support final positioning and connecting operations for segments

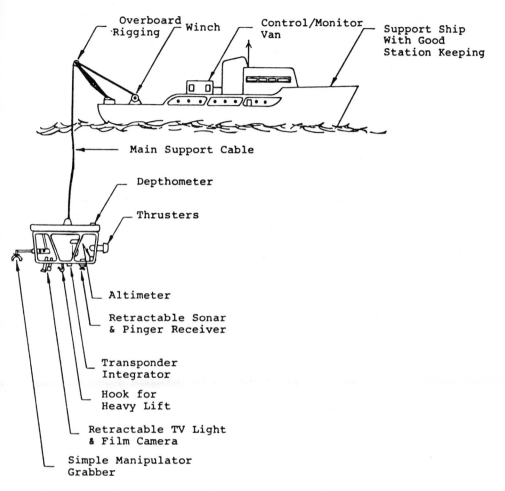

Figure 10-12 Tethered unmanned vehicle. (DUMAND Project.)

of the array. This vehicle will operate either at the end of its own dedicated power/control tether cable (Fig. 10-12) or from the short free end of a cable which is attached to the same drill string used to lower the array sections to the sea floor. The vehicle's major functions will include the following:

1. To provide local navigation, probably with a long-baseline trans-ponder system, to aid in guiding and positioning array segments before they are placed on the sea floor.

2. To provide a viewing capability to support monitoring and precise positioning during mechanical and electrical joining of the array segments. In murky water this can be done with a high-resolution

sonar, although in the clear water of the DUMAND site lights and stereo television will normally be used. For documentation purposes a still camera and strobe light will be extremely useful.

3. To provide local propulsion to support those translations and rotations necessary to make final position adjustments before array modules are placed on the sea floor.

4. With on-board manipulators, to serve as a pair of hands to make temporary physical connections, to disconnect or cut lifting lines, and to make final electrical connections. An appropriate set of quick-disconnect tools will be provided.

5. To lift relatively light objects, such as the ends of cables to be connected; for heavier objects, to assist in attachement of lifting lines between the object and either the drill string or a "skyhook" attached to a higher point on the vehicle's support cable.

In planning for use of the unmanned vehicle in deployment of the DUMAND array, it should be considered as an extension of human eyes, ears, brain, and hands to the deep sea floor. Its value will be greatest if array components are designed for this type of support, e.g., easy-grasp handles on those components which must be lifted, tugged, or rotated during final positioning.

These deployment schemes will be evaluated and modified, and new concepts developed prior to selection of a final plan. However, they provide examples for discussion of the problems to be overcome in handling and implanting large objects in the sea.

Technology Development If the actual development of a DUMAND detector is pursued, the engineering of many portions will require the utilization of the "cutting edge" of technology. To minimize cost and maximize effectiveness, the following items would be heavily technology-dependent.

Ocean Engineering. It will be necessary to define and develop components for a very large array of sensors for installation in deep water, including such items as the following.

1. Cables
2. Connectors
3. Optical and acoustic sensors
4. Precise position monitoring
5. In situ signal processing
6. Power supplies and distribution
7. Pressure-tolerant electronics applied throughout
8. Lightweight structural frameworks
9. Special materials
10. Special anchoring

In addition, procedures should be developed for installing very large arrays in deep water; large quantities of data should be processed in situ to reduce bandwidth for cable economies; unmanned vehicle expertise for inspection and repair of sensors and cabling systems in deep water should be developed; procedures must be developed for installation and maintenance of deep-sea cables and investigation of structural response in long undersea sensor strings.

Biologic Purposes.   Tools to obtain a detailed physical survey of two sites in deep water are needed, as is understanding of soil interaction in specific areas in reference to stirring, clouding, and settling as related to installation techniques and optical data gathering over long periods of time.

Technical Achievement

The study of the DUMAND requirements and its conceptualized components and procedures provides a view of synthesizing a major undersea system. It also demonstrates interactions among the requirements, the environment, the advanced technology for components, and the needed tools and equipment. If the DUMAND detector should be constructed, it will stress and thereby force the development of advanced ocean engineering systems. Thus, aside from its primary objective of providing an instrument for basic scientific research, it would also provide the ocean engineering equipment and expertise needed to solve other difficult undersea problems.

Bibliography

Booda, L. L. (1977). Trapping the elusive neutrino with a cubic mile of seawater, *Sea Technology*, Vol. 18, No. 11, November 1977.

Jones, R. S. (1978). Manned submersibles study cosmic radiation deep under the sea, *Sea Technology*, Vol. 19, No. 3, March 1978.

Learned, J. B. (1976). Neutrino search to go deep undersea?, *Physics Today*, Vol. 29, No. 4, April 1976.

Schlosser, A. J., Wilkins, G. A., and Talkington, H. R. (1979). Deployment of the 1978 DUMAND Standard Array. Presented at the 14th Pacific Science Congress, Khabarovsk, USSR, August 1979. Academy of Sciences USSR, Moscow.

Wilkins, G. (1978). *Proceedings of the 1978 DUMAND Summer Workshop*, Vol. 3, Oceanographic and Ocean Engineering Studies. Scripps Institution of Oceanography, La Jolla, Calif.

11

The Engineering Challenge
in Undersea Resource Exploitation

The expanding commercial activity in exploitation of resources from
beneath the sea provides additional opportunities for undersea work
systems. In Chapter 2, some of these commercial activities were described.
Now let us look at some new engineering challenges that lie ahead and at
how undersea work systems, their concepts and technology, might be
applied.

Subsea Completions

The production facilities for certain deep-sea oil and gas wells are being
designed for installation at the point where the pipe exits the sea floor. These
so-called "subsea completions," or "subsea production systems," include
all the piping, valving, and other flow control and safety equipment
normally installed on the surface for shallow-water operations. The problem
is that when these facilities are on the sea floor, they are not readily attainable for operations, maintenance, or modification without some type of
undersea work system.

Regardless of whether a manned or unmanned system is employed,
the key element is that special application of sensors, tools, and vehicles is

required to service these sea floor equipments. One-atmosphere dry systems have been built by Lockheed Petroleum and Shell and wet systems by Exxon, Elf Aquitaine, Cameron, Hamilton Brothers, and Vetco. While the undersea "Christmas tree" or other configured sea floor completion units appear very complex, the work required at each may be defined into a series of relatively simple tasks performed at separated but specific locations. Most of the tasks are push-pull-, rotate-, up-down-, or inspection-type operations for routine maintenance and only become more complex when modifications are required. Minor modifications such as changing valves and rerouting incoming piping can be accomplished on the sea floor. For total overhaul or replacement of the majority of the system its recovery to the sea surface is recommended.

Diver-operated systems and dry manned systems are in operation and may be considered state of the art. When the systems are totally exposed to the surrounding sea, at greater depths, careful preliminary planning must be accomplished prior to design of the sea floor unit to allow a maximum of operations to be conducted within a minimum of time and complexity of function. The points of the system that will require attention must be carefully identified and made accessible to a tool handled by a submersible vehicle (whether manned or unmanned) and the function of the task simplified and adapted to a specialized tool operated from the submersible. With special handles, wrenches, rotating claws, scrappers, and grippers, most of the maintenance tasks can be rapidly accomplished.

Assuming that the tooling has been provided that matches the tasks, then the major remaining problem is to transport the tool to the right location and in the proper orientation to do the work. This can be accomplished by applying one of the types of vehicles described earlier and by providing it with suitable sensors to find the worksite and to observe the point of action with enough optical or acoustical resolution to attach the required tool to the item to be manipulated. Again the problem comes down to selecting the type of transporter (i.e., diver, manned submersible, or unmanned vehicle) and then providing a properly designed suite of navigation, sensors, and tools to perform the task that has been carefully analyzed and defined. For some installations the "vehicle" may be nothing more than a weight that slides down a preset line to a preset location such that location and alignment are automatic. When the task is made simpler and more advanced planning is applied, then the closer the system will approach total robotic control.

Ocean Thermal Energy Conversion (OTEC)

The concept of ocean thermal energy conversion, abbreviated OTEC, is based on application of the energy available due to the temperature differential between the cold waters of the deep ocean and the warm waters at the surface. In areas such as the site selected for OTEC-1 off the west coast of the island of Hawaii, temperature differences of about 22°C (38°F) are available; the prevailing surface temperature is 26°C (78°F), whereas the temperature at depths of 1000 m (3000 ft) is 4°C (40°F). OTEC-1 is an experiment to design and install a 1-MW electrical power plant, based on the OTEC principle, that will test and evaluate heat exchanger performance. The heat exchanger of OTEC-1 will require a flow of cold water at approximately 68,200 gal/min. For this first test, state-of-the-art pipes will be utilized to draw the cold water from the ocean depths. Full-scale OTEC power plants of the future will require that a pipe about 9 m (30 ft) in diameter by 1000 m (3000 ft) in length be suspended from a surface platform. It is this cold water pipe and a shorter 61 m (200-ft) warm water discharge pipe that create the challenge to ocean engineering.

For the OTEC-1 experiment, a cluster of three 1.2-m- (4-ft-) diameter polyethylene pipes will be strapped together with synthetic fabric straps. This composite pipe will be supported by three steel cables routed down the center of the bundle and by a large flotation collar near the surface. Figure 11-1 shows the arrangement of this pipe system for OTEC-1. For future and higher-generating-capacity versions of the OTEC-type power plant, the subsurface pipes will be even larger.

The primary challenges to ocean engineering technology are involved in the development of the cold water pipe. The warm water discharge pipe has much less stringent requirements due to its shorter length. The following are engineering areas of particular concern:

Materials for the pipes themselves, the binding straps, steel support cables, flotation collar, and connecting hardware due to high stress and environmental conditions

The structural configuration of the composite pipe assembly to withstand the various vertical and horizontal loads due to sea state and ocean currents and the attachment at the top to provide support under complex dynamic conditions

Biofouling of the vertical pipes, the strainers, and the circulation piping at the surface

Station keeping of the surface support platform under all expected sea conditions while minimizing forces applied to the cold water pipe

Deployment and retrieval techniques for the cold water pipe

In situ inspection criteria and operational means

These problems serve as examples of the type of engineering challenges that must be met for future OTEC-type power plants to become feasible. A development team of Global Marine Development Inc. and TRW Ocean and Energy Systems under the direction of the Department of Energy along

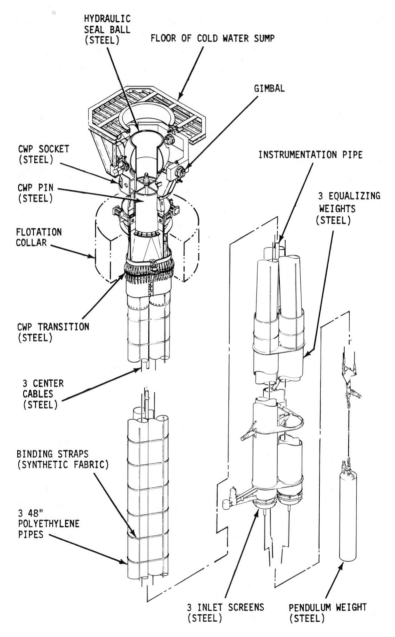

Figure 11-1 Configuration of the cold water pipe for OTEC-1. (Global Marine Development, Inc.)

with the Office of Ocean Engineering at the National Oceanic and Atmospheric Administration are working diligently on the OTEC-1 project which first put to sea in mid-1980 to start a 3-year test and evaluation program.

Undersea Blowouts

One of the greatest risks associated with undersea drilling for oil or gas is the possibility of a "blowout." While there is a vast array of safety devices, including blowout preventers (BOPs), sometimes accidents do occur. Situations such as the 1979 event off the east coast of Mexico, or earlier incidents in the Gulf of Mexico, North Sea, and off Santa Barbara, California, not only cause great losses of petroleum and large costs for cleanup but also cause long-lasting damage to the environment and to the reputation of the drilling company and its sponsor. A blowout might occur above, at, or beneath the sea floor. Each of these possibilities requires different means of correction. The major conditions to overcome are the high pressures of the uncontrolled flow of fluids and gases and the condition and location of the exit of the damaged pipe. The object is, of course, to stop the flow.

The normal approaches to this problem are to place a weighted cap over the top of the exposed pipe or to place a hollow drill rod into the offending pipe, either at the exit or below, by slant drilling and then to pump mud or concrete into it until the flow is blocked. Two alternate concepts are suggested for discussion purposes.

An unmanned remotely controlled vehicle could possibly be used to approach the site and reconnoiter the scene to determine the extent of the damage to the pipe. If conditions allow, a flexible pipe or hose could be attached to the vehicle, and the vehicle would return to the site and place a tapered nozzle into the broken pipe. Once clamped into position, concrete or mud could then be pumped into the pipe to block the flow.

An alternate approach could be applied if a portion of the intact pipe casing were extending above the sea floor. In this case, a specially prepared hydraulic press would be carried to the pipe by the undersea vehicle and placed around it and hydraulic power applied over a relatively long length of the pipe; this would crush the pipe, thereby blocking the flow. This technique might also be employed to reduce oil flow so that an easier approach might be made to the mouth of the offending pipe in order to insert a hose for concrete placement, as already described.

The possible application of undersea work systems in the environment of a blowout requires some specialized preparation. The following are the items that would most need attention:

Due to the danger inherent in this type of operation, only an unmanned system should be considered.

The undersea vehicle would be required to have very high thrust to be able to maneuver successfully in the turbulent underwater conditions caused by the high flow of the oil and gas.

An acoustic imaging system would most likely be required since poor visibility due to the oil and to the stirring up of the sediments from the sea floor by the turbulence would be expected.

The forward part of the vehicle and its tool holder for the hydraulic press, hose, and clamping device would have to be very rugged to withstand violent bumping, because the final approach to the pipe might have to be made "blind" or "by feel" due to lack of visibility.

The hydraulic press and hose with its attaching clamps would be of fairly straightforward design once the conditions of the blowout are ascertained.

This suggested technique, including application of undersea work systems, provides another example of the procedures that are required when preparing for undersea operations. That is, one must determine the condition of the worksite; ascertain the task to be accomplished; select the best transporter for the conditions to be encountered; define the sensors required to get to the worksite and to monitor the performance of the task; prepare the specialized tools to perform the defined tasks and interface these to the regular manipulators that are part of the vehicle system; and then with a carefully detailed step-by-step plan proceed to do the job.

Bibliography

Bender, E. (1979). The OTEC gamble, goal: Commercial power production by 1990, *Sea Technology*, Vol. 20, No. 8, August 1979.

Hove, D., and Grote, P. (1979). Preliminary designs of OTEC cold water pipe for grazing and moored plants, in *Proceedings Oceans '79*. Institute of Electrical and Electronic Engineers, Inc., San Diego.

Kaplan, P. (1979). Wave drift forces on OTEC platforms, in *Proceedings Marine Technology '79, Ocean Energy*. The Marine Technology Society, Washington, D.C.

Little, B. (1979). A biofouling study of ocean thermal energy conversion (OTEC) heat exchanger candidate metals, in *Proceedings Marine Technology '79, Ocean Energy*. The Marine Technology Society, Washington, D.C.

McGuinness, T., and Scotti, R. S. (1979). OTEC cold water pipe: Program, problems and procedures, in *Proceedings Marine Technology '79, Ocean Energy*. The Marine Technology Society, Washington, D.C.

Noroil (1979). Subsea systems, *Noroil*, Vol. 7, June 1979.

Ocean Industry (1977). Special issue on subsea systems, *Ocean Industry*, Vol. 12, No. 7, July 1977.

Ramsden, H. D., and Svenson, N. A. (1979). Ocean thermal energy conversion early test program (OTEC-1), in *Proceedings Marine Technology '79, Ocean Energy.* The Marine Technology Society, Washington, D.C.

Thornton, D. (1977). Industry facing up to subsea complexities, *Ocean Resources Engineering, Vol. 11, No. 2, April 1977.*

Index